COLOR VISION

An Enduring Problem in Psychology

SELECTED READINGS

Edited by

RICHARD C. TEEVAN
Bucknell University
AND
ROBERT C. BIRNEY
Amherst College

AN INSIGHT BOOK

D. VAN NOSTRAND COMPANY, INC.

PRINCETON, NEW JERSEY

TORONTO LONDON

Van Nostrand Regional Offices:
New York, Chicago, San Francisco

D. Van Nostrand Company, Ltd., London

D. Van Nostrand Company (Canada), Ltd., Toronto

Published simultaneously in Canada by
D. Van Nostrand Company (Canada), Ltd.

Foreword

In the field of psychology we believe that the student ought to get the "feel" of experimentation by reading original source materials. In this way he can acquire a better understanding of the discipline by seeing scientific ideas grow and change. However, one of the main problems in teaching is the limited availability of these sources, which communicate most effectively the personality of the author and the excitement of ongoing research.

For these reasons we have decided to edit several books,* each devoted to a particular problem in psychology. In every case we attempt to select problems that have been and are controversial—that have been and still are alive. We intend to present these problems as a set of selected original articles which are arranged in historical order and in order of progress in the field. We believe that it is important for the student to see that theories and researches build on what has gone before; that one study leads to another, that theory leads to research and then to revision of theory. We believe that *telling* the student this does not make the same kind of impression as letting him see it happen in actuality. This is the rationale behind this series of problems books. Editor's remarks are kept to the absolute minimum. The idea is for the student to read and build ideas for himself. (It should also be pointed out that articles deemed too technical are not included.)

SUGGESTIONS FOR USE

These readings books can be used by the student in either of two ways. They are organized so that, with the help of the instructor (or of the students if used in seminars), a topic can be covered at length and in depth. This would necessitate lectures or discussions on articles not covered in the series to fill in the gaps. On the other hand, each book taken alone will give a student a good

* (Pub. note: to be a sub-series within the Insight Book Series)

iii

idea of the problem being covered and its historical background as well as its present state and the direction it seems to be taking. At the risk of being repetitious, we would like to say again that we believe it is important for the student to see how theories and researches lead to other researches and revision of theories. It is also important for the student to become familiar with significant researches at first hand. It is to these ideas that this sub-series on enduring problems in psychology is dedicated.

Amherst, Mass.   R.C.B.
Lewisburg, Pa.   R.C.T.
January, 1961

Contents

PART I

1. THE THEORY OF LIGHT AND COLOR   3
   by Thomas Young
2. ON PHYSICAL OPTICS   7
   by Thomas Young
3. THE SENSATIONS OF VISION   10
   by Hermann von Helmholtz
4. PRINCIPLES OF A NEW THEORY OF THE COLOR SENSE   28
   by Ewald Hering
5. EXAMINATION OF A TOTAL COLOR-BLIND   32
   by Ewald Hering
6. COLOR BLINDNESS   40
   by Adolf Fick
7. A NEW THEORY OF LIGHT-SENSATION   47
   by Christine Ladd-Franklin
8. BEARING OF RESULTS ON THEORIES OF COLOR-VISION   53
   by Mary Collins

PART II

9. THE DEVELOPMENT OF THOMAS YOUNG'S THEORY OF COLOR VISION   61
   by Selig Hecht
10. THE THEORY OF COLOUR VISION   86
    by Robert A. Houston
11. A PHYSIOLOGICAL THEORY OF COLOUR PERCEPTION   90
    by Ragnar Granit
12. GENERAL STATEMENT OF THE THEORY   99
    by Edward N. Willmer
13. RECENT ADVANCES IN COLOUR VISION   102
    by Hamilton Hartridge
14. AN OPPONENT-PROCESS THEORY OF COLOR VISION   113
    by Leo M. Hurvich and Dorothea Jameson

v

15. COLOR DEFECT AND COLOR THEORY   138
        by Clarence H. Graham and Yun Hsia
16. EXPERIMENTS IN COLOR VISION   162
        by Edwin H. Land
17. VISION   184
        by Charles E. Osgood

Introduction

This volume deals with the way man perceives color. We feel that the selection of articles is such that it can be read with profit by anyone with an interest in color and how man perceives it. In order to make this possible, many articles, especially by physicists, were not included even though they had something to offer to the study of color vision. These would have been too complex for the layman or for the average student in experimental perception courses. This volume does not profess to be a handbook for the professional in this field; we believe it does give the beginner and the moderately advanced student a good idea of the field.

In the first section of this book, we have selected readings from the classical theorists of color vision. These run from Thomas Young to Christine Ladd-Franklin. We have then used a selection from Mary Collins which evaluates these theories (up to the 1920's). We have used color blindness as an evaluation of theories since all of the theorists try to handle this subject in one way or another—which is not true of all of the devices we might have used.

The second section is devoted to the various ways that theorists have tried to explain color perception from the 1920's to the present. We have placed them in chronological order since the methods of handling the data are so different that no other way was feasible. We have ended with an overview of the field that is out of place chronologically since we could find no more recent summary that would be as comprehensible to the unsophisticated reader. We believe that this article does an excellent job of laying out the problems, and that the fact that it does not cover some of the latest articles (Edwin Land, for example, in this volume) does not constitute too much of a handicap.

Where we have thought it necessary in order to facilitate understanding, we have inserted editorial notes at the beginning of some articles. Some of the works are excerpted, which means that the reader may feel that he is moving into the middle of an argument. We have tried to minimize this feeling as much as possible but, when trying to cover a field within a given number of pages, this turns out to be necessary.

As usual, we make no claim to have made ideal selection of articles to place the field of color vision before you. However, within the limits of the population for whom this volume is intended, we have done the best job that we knew how to do.

Part 1

I

On the Theory of Light and Color

THOMAS YOUNG

In these two excerpts from his lectures, we find Thomas
Young building a theory of color vision that has existed
to the present day. We have not included the work of
Sir Isaac Newton, although Young obviously builds upon
him, because Young has included copious quotations of
the most relevant portions of Newton's writings.

Here, then, is what we consider to be the beginning
of modern color theory. In the first excerpt Young makes
the oft-quoted point that three color receptors are prob-
ably enough to account for color vision. The second ex-
cerpt contains the Young theory of color vision.

HYPOTHESIS III.

The Sensation of different Colours depends on
the different frequency of Vibrations, excited
by Light in the Retina.

Passages from NEWTON.

"The objector's hypothesis, as to the fundamental part of it,
is not against me. That fundamental supposition is, that the
parts of bodies, when briskly agitated, do excite vibrations in
the ether, which are propagated every way from those bodies
in straight lines, and cause a sensation of light by beating and
dashing against the bottom of the eye, something after the
manner that vibrations in the air cause a sensation of sound by
beating against the organs of hearing. Now, the most free and
natural application of this hypothesis to the solution of phe-

This selection is taken from Thomas Young, "On the Theory
of Light and Colours," from *Lectures in Natural Philosophy*,
London: Printed for Joseph Johnson, St. Paul's Churchyard,
by William Savage, 1907, pp. 613-632.

3

nomena, I take to be this: that the agitated parts of bodies, according to their several sizes, figures, and motions, do excite vibrations in the ether of various depths or bignesses, which, being promiscuously propagated through that medium to our eyes, effect in us a sensation of light of a white colour; but if by any means those of unequal bignesses be separated from one another, the largest beget a sensation of a red colour, the least or shortest of a deep violet, and the intermediate ones of intermediate colours; much after the manner that bodies, according to their several sizes, shapes, and motions, excite vibrations in the air of various bignesses, which, according to those bignesses, make several tones in sound: that the largest vibrations are best able to overcome the resistance of a refracting superficies, and so break through it with least refraction; whence the vibrations of several bignesses, that is, the rays of several colours, which are blended together in light, must be parted from one another by refraction, and so cause the phenomena of prisms, and other refracting substances; and that it depends on the thickness of a thin transparent plate or bubble, whether a vibration shall be reflected at its further superficies, or transmitted; so that, according to the number of vibrations, interceding the two superficies, they may be reflected or transmitted for many successive thicknesses. And, since the vibrations which make blue and violet, are supposed shorter than those which make red and yellow, they must be reflected at a less thickness of the plate: which is sufficient to explicate all the ordinary phenomena of those plates or bubbles, and also of all natural bodies, whose parts are like so many fragments of such plates. These seem to be the most plain, genuine, and necessary conditions of this hypothesis. And they agree so justly with my theory, that if the animadversor think fit to apply them, he need not, on that account, apprehend a divorce from it. But yet, how he will defend it from other difficulties, I know not." (Phil. Trans. Vol. VII, p. 5088. Abr. Vol. I, p. 145. Nov. 1672.)

"To explain colours, I suppose, that as bodies of various sizes, densities, or sensations, do by percussion or other action excite sounds of various tones, and consequently vibrations in the air of different bigness; so the rays of light, by impinging on the stiff refracting superficies, excite vibrations in the ether, —of various bigness; the biggest, strongest, or most potent rays, the largest vibrations; and others shorter, according to their bigness, strength, or power: and therefore the ends of the capillamenta of the optic nerve, which pave or face the retina, being such refracting superficies, when the rays impinge upon them, they must there excite these vibrations, which vibrations (like those of sound in a trunk or trumpet) will run along the aqueous pores or crystalline pith of the capillamenta, through the optic nerves, into the sensorium;—and there, I suppose, affect the sense with various colours, according to their bigness and mixture; the biggest with the strongest colours, reds and yellows; the least with the weakest, blues and violets; the middle with green; and a confusion of all with white, much after the manner that, in the sense of hearing, nature makes use of aerial vibrations of several bignesses, to generate sounds of divers tones; for the analogy of nature is to be observed." (BIRCH Vol. III, p. 262. Dec. 1675.)

"Considering the lastingness of the motions excited in the bottom of the eye by light, are they not of a vibrating nature? —Do not the most refrangible rays excite the shortest vibrations,—the least refrangible the largest? May not the harmony and discord of colours arise from the proportions of the vibrations propagated through the fibres of the optic nerve into the brain, as the harmony and discord of sounds arise from the proportions of the vibrations of the air?" (Optics, Qu. 16, 13, 14.)

Scholium. Since, for the reason here assigned by NEWTON, it is probable that the motion of the retina is rather of a vibratory than of an undulatory nature, the frequency of the vibrations must be dependent on the constitution of this substance. Now, as it is almost impossible to conceive each sensitive point of the retina to contain an infinite number of particles, each capable of vibrating in perfect unison with every possible undulation, it becomes necessary to suppose the number limited, for instance, to the three principal colours, red, yellow, and blue, of which the undulations are related in magnitude nearly as the numbers 8, 7, and 6; and that each of the particles is capable of being put in motion less or more forcibly, by undulations differing less or more from a perfect unison; for instance, the undulations of green light being nearly in the ratio of 6½, will affect equally the particles in unison with yellow and blue, and produce the same effect as a light composed of those two species: and each sensitive filament of the nerve may consist of three portions, one for each principal colour. Allowing this statement, it appears that any attempt to produce a musical effect from colours, must be unsuccessful, or at least that nothing more than a very simple melody could be imita-

ted by them; for the period, which in fact constitutes
the harmony of any concord, being a multiple of the
periods of the single undulations, would in this case be
wholly without the limits of sympathy of the retina, and
would lose its effect; in the same manner as the harmony
of a third or a fourth is destroyed, by depressing it to
the lowest notes of the audible scale. In hearing, there
seems to be no permanent vibration of any part of the
organ.

2

On Physical Optics

THOMAS YOUNG

Sir Isaac Newton observed that the effect of white light on the sense of sight might be imitated by a mixture of colours taken from different parts of the spectrum, notwithstanding the omission of some of the rays naturally belonging to white light. Thus, if we intercept one half of each of the four principal portions into which the spectrum is divided, the remaining halves will still preserve, when mixed together, the appearance of whiteness; so that it is probable, that the different parts of those portions of the spectrum, which appear of one colour, have precisely the same effect on the eye. It is certain that the perfect sensations of yellow and of blue are produced respectively, by mixtures of red and green and of green and violet light, and there is reason to suspect that those sensations are always compounded of the separate sensations combined; at least, this supposition simplifies the theory of colours: it may, therefore, be adopted with advantage, until it be found inconsistent with any of the phenomena; and we may consider white light as composed of a mixture of red, green, and violet only, in the proportion of about two parts red, four green, and one violet, with respect to the quantity or intensity of the sensations produced.*

This selection is taken from Thomas Young, "On Physical Optics," from A Course of Lectures on Natural Philosophy and the Mechanical Arts, Vol. I, London: printed for Taylor and Welton, Upper Gower Street, 1845, pp. 344-345.

* So Wunsch, Versuche über die Farben, Leipz, 1792. Mayer, in an essay De Affinitate Colorum, pub. 1722, refers all colours to red, yellow, and blue: and this is the more common hypothesis. See Guyot, Recreations, Par. 1769. Goethe,

If we mix together, in proper proportions, any substances exhibiting these colours in their greatest purity, and place the mixture in a light sufficiently strong, we obtain the appearance of perfect whiteness; but in a fainter light the mixture is grey, or of that hue which arises from a combination of white and black; black bodies being such as reflect white light but in a very scanty proportion. For the same reason, green and red substances mixed together usually make rather a brown than a yellow colour, and many yellow colours, when laid on very thickly, or mixed with black, become brown. The sensations of various kinds of light may also be combined in a still more satisfactory manner, by painting the surface of a circle with different colours, in any way that may be desired, and causing it to revolve with such rapidity, that the whole may assume the appearance of a single tint, or of a combination of tints, resulting from the mixture of the colours.

From three simple sensations, with their combinations, we obtain seven primitive distinctions of colours; but the different proportions in which they may be combined, afford a variety of tints beyond all calculation. The three simple sensations being red, green, and violet, the three binary combinations are yellow, consisting of red and green; crimson, of red and violet; and blue, of green and violet; and the seventh in order is white light, composed by all the three united. But the blue thus produced, by combining the whole of the green and violet rays, is not the blue of the spectrum, for four parts of green and one of violet make a blue, differing very little from green; while the blue of the spectrum appears to contain as much violet as green; and it is for this reason that red and blue usually make a purple, deriving its hue from the predominance of the violet.

It would be possible to exhibit at once to the eye the combinations of any three colours in all imaginable varieties. Two of them might be laid down on a revolving surface, in the form of triangles, placed in opposite direc-

---

Farbenlehre, 1810. Brewster, *Tr. Roy. Soc. Ed.* xii. 123. Nollett, *Leçons de Physique*, v. 388, considers the three colours to be orange, green, and indigo.

tions, and the third on projections perpendicular to the surface, which, while the eye remained at rest in any one point, obliquely situated, would exhibit more or less of their painted sides, as they passed through their different angular positions; and the only further alteration, that could be produced in any of the tints, would be derived from the different degrees of light only. The same effect may also be exhibited by mixing the colours in different proportions, by means of the pencil, beginning from three equidistant points as the centres of the respective colours.

3

The Sensations of Vision

HERMANN VON HELMHOLTZ

Every difference of impression made by light, as we
have seen, may be regarded as a function of three independent variables; and the three variables which have
been chosen thus far were (1) the luminosity, (2) the
hue, and (3) the saturation, or (1) the quantity of white,
(2) the quantity of some colour of the spectrum, and
(3) the wave-length of this colour. However, instead of
these variables, three others may also be employed; and
in fact this is what it amounts to, when all colours are
regarded as being mixtures of variable amounts of *three
so-called fundamental colours,* which are generally taken
to be *red, yellow* and *blue.* To conceive this theory ob-
jectively, and to assert that there are simple colours in the
spectrum which can be combined to produce a visual
impression that will be the same as that produced by any
other simple or compound light, would not be correct.
There are no such three simple colours that can be combined to match the other colours of the spectrum
even fairly well, because the colours of the spectrum
invariably appear to be more saturated than the composite colours. Least suited for this purpose are red,
yellow and blue; for if we take for blue a colour like
the hue of the sky, and not a more greenish blue, it will
be impossible to get green at all by mixing these colours.
By taking a greenish yellow and a greenish blue, the best
we can get is a very pale green. These three colours would
not have been selected, had it not been that most per-

This selection is taken from H. von Helmoltz, *Physiological
Optics,* 3rd edition, Vol. II (Translated by J. P. C. Southall);
Optical Society of America, pp. 141-154. Reprinted by per-
mission.

sons, relying on the mixture of pigments, made the mistake of thinking that a mixture of yellow and blue light gives green. It would be rather better to take *violet*, *green* and *red* for fundamental colours. Blue can be obtained by mixing violet and green, but it is not the saturated blue of the spectrum; and a dead yellow can be made with green and red, which is not at all like the brilliant yellow in the spectrum.

If we think of the colours as plotted on a colour-chart by the method sketched above, it is evident from the rules given for the construction that all colours that are to be made by mixing three colours must be contained within the triangle whose vertices are the places in the

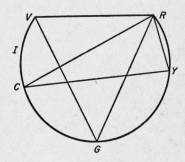

Fig. 20.

chart where the three fundamental colours are. Thus, in the adjoining colour circle (Fig. 20), where the positions of the colours are indicated by the initial letters of their names (I = indigo-blue, C = cyan-blue, Y = yellow, G = green, etc.), all the colours that can be made by mixing red, cyan-blue and yellow are comprised within the triangle RCY. Thus, as we see, two large pieces of the circle are missing, and all that could be obtained would be a very pale violet and a very pale green. But if, instead of cyan-blue, the colour of the blue sky, indigo-blue, were taken, green would be missing entirely. The triangle VRG comprises the colours obtained by mixing violet, red and green, and a larger number of the existing colours would indeed be represented. But, as the diagram shows, large portions of the circle are still missing, as must always be the case according to the results of experiments on the mixture of the colours of the spectrum. The conclusion is that the boundary of the colour chart must be a curved line which differs considerably from the perimeter of the triangle.

BREWSTER, endeavoring to defend the objective nature of three fundamental colours, maintained that for every wave-length there were three different kinds of light, red, yellow and blue, mixed merely in different proportions so as to give the different colours of the spectrum. Thus, the colours of the spectrum were considered as being compound colours consisting of three kinds of light of different quality; although the degree of refrangibility of the rays was the same for each individual simple colour. BREWSTER's idea was that light of all three fundamental colours could be proved to exist in the different simple colours by the absorption of light by coloured media. His entire theory is based on this conception, which was shown in the preceding chapter to be erroneous.

Apart from BREWSTER's hypothesis, the notion of three fundamental colours as having any objective significance has no meaning anyhow. For as long as it is simply a question of physical relations, and the human eye is left out of the game, the properties of the compound light are dependent only on the relative amounts of light of all the separate wave-lengths it contains. When we speak of reducing the colours to three fundamental colours, this must be understood in a subjective sense and as being an attempt to trace the *colour sensations* to three *fundamental sensations*. This was the way that YOUNG regarded the problem;[1] and, in fact, his

---

[1] MAXWELL in his lecture "On colour vision" at the Royal Institution (see *Scientific Papers* of JAMES CLERK MAXWELL, II, pp. 266-279), speaking of YOUNG's theory, says:

"We may state it thus:—We are capable of feeling three different colour-sensations. Light of different kinds excites these sensations in different proportions, and it is by the different combinations of these three primary sensations that all the varieties of visible colour are produced. In this statement there is one word on which we must fix our attention. That word is, Sensation. It seems almost a truism to say that colour is a

theory affords an exceedingly simple and clear explanation of all the phenomena of the physiological colour theory. He supposes that:

1. The eye is provided with three distinct sets of nervous fibres. Stimulation of the first excites the sensation of red, stimulation of the second the sensation of green, and stimulation of the third the sensation of violet.

2. Objective homogeneous light excites these kinds of fibres in various degrees, depending on its wave-length. The red-sensitive fibres are stimulated most by light of longest wave-length, and the violet-sensitive fibres by light of shortest wave-length. But this does not mean that each colour of the spectrum does not stimulate all

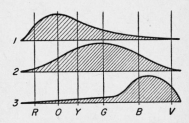

Fig. 21.

three kinds of fibres, some feebly and others strongly; on the contrary, in order to explain a series of phenomena, it is necessary to assume that that is exactly what does happen. Suppose that the colours of the spectrum are plotted horizontally in Fig. 21 in their natural sequence, from

sensation; and yet YOUNG, by honestly recognizing this elementary Truth established the first consistent theory of colour. So far as I know, THOMAS YOUNG was the first who, starting from the well-known fact that there are three primary colours, sought for the explanation of this fact, not in the nature of light, but in the constitution of man. Even of those who have written on colour since the time of Young, some have supposed that they ought to study the properties of pigments, and others that they ought to analyze the rays of light. They have sought for a knowledge of colour by examining something in external nature —something out of themselves." (J. P. C. S.)

red to violet, the three curves may be taken to indicate something like the degree of excitation of the three kinds of fibres, No. 1 for the red-sensitive fibres, No. 2 for the green-sensitive fibres, and No. 3 for the violet-sensitive fibres.

Pure *red* light stimulates the red-sensitive fibres strongly and the two other kinds of fibres feebly; giving the sensation red.

Pure *yellow* light stimulates the red-sensitive and green-sensitive fibres moderately and the violet-sensitive fibres feebly; giving the sensation yellow.

Pure *green* light stimulates the green-sensitive fibres strongly, and the two other kinds much more feebly; giving the sensation green.

Pure *blue* light stimulates the green-sensitive and violet-sensitive fibres moderately, and the red-sensitive fibres feebly; giving the sensation blue.

Pure *violet* light stimulates the violet-sensitive fibres strongly, and the other fibres feebly; giving the sensation violet.

When all the fibres are stimulated about equally, the sensation is that of *white* or pale hues.

It might be natural to suppose that on this hypothesis the number of nervous fibres and nerve-endings would have to be trebled, as compared with the number ordinarily assumed when each single fibre is made to conduct all possible colour stimulations. However, in the writer's opinion there is nothing in Young's hypothesis that is opposed to the anatomical facts in this respect; because we are entirely ignorant as to the number of conducting fibres, and there are also quantities of other microscopical elements (cells, nuclei, rods) to which hitherto no specific functions could be ascribed. But this is not the essential thing in Young's hypothesis. That appears to the writer to consist rather in the idea of the colour sensations being composed of three processes in the nervous substance that are perfectly independent of one another. This independence is manifested not merely in the phenomena which are being considered at present but also in those of fatigue of the nervous mechanism of vision. It would not be absolutely necessary to assume different nervous fibres for these different sensations. So far as mere explanation is concerned, the same advantages that are afforded by YOUNG's hypothesis could be gained by supposing that within each individual fibre there might occur three activities all different from and independent of one another. But the form of this hypothesis as originally proposed by YOUNG is clearer in both conception and expression than it would be if it were modified as suggested, and hence it will be retained in its original concrete form, for the sake of exposition if for nothing else. Nowhere in the physical (electrical) phenomena of nervous stimulation either in the sensory or motor nerves can there be detected any such differentiation of activity as must exist if each fibre of the optic nerve has to transmit all the colour sensations. By YOUNG's hypothesis it is possible even in this connection to transfer directly to the optic nerve the simple conceptions as to the mechanism of the stimulation and its conduction which we were led to form at first by studying the phenomena in the motor nerves. This would not be the case on the assumption that each fibre of the optic nerve has to sustain three different kinds of states of stimulation which do not mutually interfere with one another. YOUNG's hypothesis is only a more special application of the law of specific sense energies. Just as tactile sensation and visual sensation in the eye are demonstrably affairs of different nervous fibres, the same thing is assumed here too with respect to the various sensations of the fundamental colours.

The choice of the three fundamental colours is somewhat arbitrary. Any three colours which can be mixed to get white might be chosen. YOUNG may have been guided by the consideration that the terminal colours of the spectrum seem to have special claims by virtue of their positions. If they were not chosen, one of the fundamental colours would have to have a purplish hue, and the curve corresponding to it in Fig. 21 would have two maxima, one in the red and one in the violet. This would be a more complicated assumption, but not an impossible one. So far as the writer can see, the only other way of determining one of the fundamental colours would be by investigating the colour-blind. To what extent such investigation confirms YOUNG's hypothesis for red at least, will be shown later.

That each of the three chosen fundamental colours of the spectrum stimulates not only the nervous fibres that are designated by the same name as the colour in question but the other fibres also in a less degree, has been already proved by the results of colour mixture, certainly in the case of green. For if we think of all the colour sensations that are composed of the three fundamental

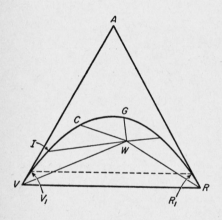

Fig. 22.

colours as being plotted on a plane chart according to NEWTON's system, it follows from what has been stated above that the colour area must be enclosed in a triangle. This triangle must include within it the colour area shown in Fig. 22 which comprises all colours that are miscible from the colours of the spectrum. It would be possible to do this by shifting the sensation of pure green towards A, as in done in Fig. 22, on the assumption that spectrum red and violet, R and V, are pure fundamental colours. In this case the colour triangle that contains within it all possible colour sensation would be AVR. This assumption, as stated, would satisfy the actual facts of colour mixture. On the other hand, however, certain other facts to be mentioned presently, in connection with colour blindness and the change of hue due to increase of intensity of the light and the phenomena of after-images, render it necessary to assume that neither spectrum red nor violet corresponds to a simple sensation of one fundamental colour, but to a slightly mixed sensation. Accordingly, the positions of spectrum red and violet in the colour triangle Fig. 22 would have to be displaced about to R_i and V_i and the closed curve $ICYR_iV_i$ would then embrace all possible colours of objective light.

Thence it follows that there must be a series of colour sensations still more saturated than those which are evoked under ordinary circumstances by objective light, even by that of the spectrum. In Fig. 22 the colours aroused in the normal eye by external light are comprised within the area bounded by the curve and the straight line V_iR_i. The rest of the triangle corresponds to colour sensations that cannot be excited directly by external light. Since these latter sensations are all farther separated from white than the colours of the spectrum, they must be even more saturated than those colours themselves, which are the most saturated objective colours of which we have any knowledge. And, as a matter of fact, when we come to the theory of after-images, produced by fatiguing the eye by the complementary colours, we shall see how to produce colour sensations beside which the colours of the spectrum look pale.

The fact above mentioned, that the different colours of the spectrum do not appear to be all saturated to the same degree, is easily explained by this theory.

The eyes of some individuals are not able to distinguish as many colours as those of ordinary persons. The visual perceptions in cases of *colour blindness* (*achromatopia, achrupsia*) are of particular interest for the theory of colour sensations. A. SEEBECK has demonstrated that there are two classes of colour-blind people. Individuals belonging to each group confuse the same set of colours, and differ from each other merely in the degree of their difficulty. On the other hand, individuals in one class recognize most of the mistakes made by those of the other class.

The most numerous cases, especially in England, appear to belong to SEEBECK's second division. Their trouble is often called *Daltonism* (or *anerythropsia*, by GOETHE), after the celebrated chemist J. DALTON, who himself belonged to this group and was the first to investigate this condition carefully.[1] As some English scientists have protested against this mode of perpetuating the name of their renowned countryman by one of his defects, let us call this condition *red blindness*.[2] Individuals in whom it is completely developed see only two colours in the spectrum, which they usually describe as blue and yellow. They include in the latter all of the red, orange, yellow and green. They call the green-blue hues grey, and the remainder blue. They do not see the extreme red at all when it is faint, but they may do so when it is intense. Thus, they usually put the red end of the spectrum at a place where normal eyes still see distinctly a faint red. In pigments they confuse *red* (that is, vermilion and reddish orange) with *brown* and *green*; whereas to the normal eye in general the confused red hues are much brighter than the brown and green. They cannot distinguish between *golden yellow* and *yellow* or between *pink-red* and *blue*. On the other hand, all mixtures of different colours that appear alike to the normal eye appear alike also to the red-blind. With regard to DALTON's case, Sir J. HERSCHEL[3] has already advanced the opinion, that all colours discriminated by him might be considered as being com-

---

[1] According to more modern determinations, SEEBECK's second form of colour blindness, called "green blindness" by HELMHOLTZ, is more frequent, and the only reason why it is more often unnoticed than "red blindness" is because its symptoms are rather less striking. As to new suggestions for designating the forms of colour blindness, see the section on this subject in the appendices at the end of this volume.—N.

[2] Red-blind individuals, as HELMHOLTZ calls them, are termed *protanopes* by v. KRIES, and green-blind *deuteranopes*. (J. P. C. S.)

[3] In a letter quoted in G. WILSON, *On colour Blindness*. Edinburgh 1855. p. 60.

posed of two fundamental colours instead of three.[4] This view has been recently confirmed by MAXWELL by his method of measuring colours with the mixtures on the colour top. In the case of a healthy eye, as has been shown, a colour match may be formed between any given colour and three suitably chosen fundamental colours, plus white and black. In case of red-blind persons, as the writer himself has verified, only two colours are needed besides white and black (for instance, yellow and blue) to make a colour match on the colour top with any other colour.

In the author's experiments with Mr. M., who was a student in the polytechnic institute, accustomed to physical investigations and fairly sensitive to such differences of colour as he could still recognize at all, chrome yellow and ultramarine were used as principal colours. A mixture on the colour top of 35° of yellow and 325° of black, which was olive-green to an average person, seemed to him identical with a *red* about like that of sealing wax. The experiments indicated that a mixture of 327° of yellow and 33° of blue, which looks grey-yellow to the normal eye, was to him the same as *green* of hue about corresponding to the line E in the spectrum. And 165° of yellow mixed with 195° of blue, which ordinarily gives a faint reddish grey, was the same to him as *grey*. As all other hues could be mixed from red, yellow, green, and blue, the result was that, so far as Mr. M. was concerned, they could all be obtained by mixing yellow and blue.

From GRASSMANN's laws of colour mixture, as applied to an eye that confuses red with green, it follows directly that the hues which it does differentiate can all be obtained by mixing two other colours, say, yellow and blue. For if red and green appear to be the same, necessarily all mixtures of these two colours will appear to be the same. Moreover, since colours that look alike produce a mixture that looks like them, every mixture of a given amount of yellow with a given amount of any one of the

---

[4] These types of colour blindness have colour systems that are functions of two variables, whereas normal colour vision, as has been stated, is a function of three variables. Thus normal individuals are said to be *trichomats* as distinguished from these abnormal *dichromats*. (J. P. C. S.)

colours made by mixing red and green, which has the same appearance to a colour-blind person, will give a resultant colour that looks the same to him. But for the healthy eye one of the colours obtained by mixing red and green can be made also by mixing yellow and blue; and hence for the colour-blind eye this colour can be substituted for all combinations of red and green. Consequently, all mixtures of yellow, red and green may be produced also by mixing yellow and blue, so far as the colour-blind eye is concerned; and the same thing may be proved likewise for all mixtures of blue, red and green. And, lastly, since all hues for the healthy eye can be obtained by mixing red, yellow, green and blue, all hues for the colour-blind eye can be obtained by mixing yellow and blue.

If the colours are plotted on a plane chart by the method of constructing the centres of gravity, all such colours as appear to a colour-blind person to be the same at suitable luminosity will be ranged along a straight line, since a mixture of two colours must be on the straight line joining these two points, and the mixture must appear to have the same hue as its components, if the latter look alike. Moreover, it may be proved that all these straight lines intersect in one point (which may be at infinity, in which case they will all be parallel), and that the colour corresponding to this point must be invisible to the colour-blind eye.

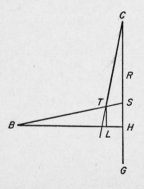

Fig. 23.

To the colour-blind person the quantity r of the colour at R in Fig. 23 appears the same as the quantity g of the colour at G. Now

$$r = nr + (1 - n)r.$$

The quantity ng of the colour G looks just like the quantity nr of the colour R. Thus, supposing that n is a proper fraction, the quantity r of the colour R appears the same as the mixture of the quantity $(1 - n)r$ of the colour R with the quantity ng of the colour G. In the colour chart this mixed colour will be at the point S in the line RG such that

$$RS : SG = ng : (1 - n)r \quad . \quad . \quad . \quad (1)$$

and the quantity of this mixed colour will be

$$s = ng + (1 - n)r.$$

So far as the colour-blind eye is concerned, the appearance of this colour will not depend on the value of n.

Suppose now that the quantity b of the colour B is mixed with the quantity s of the colour S; the result will be a mixed colour whose appearance to the colour-blind eye is independent of the variable magnitude n. Let T be the place of this mixed colour in the chart and t its quantity; then

$$t = b + s = b + ng + (1 - n)r$$
$$TS : BT = b : s = b : [ng + (1 - n)r] \quad . \quad . \quad (1a)$$

From B let fall the perpendicular BH on RG and from T the perpendicular TL on BH; and put

$$
\begin{aligned}
LH &= x & BH &= h \\
TL &= y & HG &= a \\
& & RG &= c
\end{aligned}
$$

Then by (1a):

$$\frac{x}{h} = \frac{LH}{BH} = \frac{TS}{BS} = \frac{b}{b + ng + (1 - n)r} \quad . \quad . \quad . \quad (1b)$$

$$\frac{y}{h - x} = \frac{TL}{BL} = \frac{SH}{BH} = \frac{SG - a}{h}.$$

Since from equation (1)

$$SG = c \cdot \frac{(1-n)r}{ng + (1-n)r},$$

therefore

$$\frac{y}{h-x} = \frac{(c-a)(1-n)r - ang}{h[ng + (1-n)r]} \quad \ldots \quad (1c)$$

Eliminating the variable n from (1b) and (1c), we obtain an equation connecting the rectangular coördinates of the point T, as follows:

$$0 = ybh(g-r) - x[crg + br(c-a) + abg] \\ + bh[(c-a)r + ag] \ldots \quad (1d)$$

As this is a linear equation between x and y, the locus of the point T is a straight line, and all the mixed colours that lie on this line appear to be the same to the colour-blind eye. Suppose TQ is this straight line meeting the straight line RG in the point designated by Q; then the value of y for $x = 0$ will be $QH = y_0$ as given by the equation

$$y_0 = \frac{(c-a)r + ag}{r - g} \quad \ldots \ldots \quad (1e)$$

This value of y_0 is independent of the amount b of the colour that is to be mixed with S; and every straight line that is the locus of points corresponding to colours that all look alike, obtained by mixing the colours R, G and B, will pass through this point Q; and in case $r = g$, that is, when y_0 becomes infinite, the point Q will be the infinitely distant point of the straight line RG, and the system of lines TQ will be a pencil of parallel lines.

The distance of Q from the point R is

$$y_0 - c + a = \frac{cg}{r - g} = QR \quad \ldots \ldots \quad (1f)$$

When an amount q of the colour Q is mixed with the amount g of the colour G so as to make the colour R, then we must have

$$\frac{QR}{RG} = \frac{g}{q}$$

and therefore by equation (1f), since RG =c:

$$\frac{g}{r-q} = \frac{g}{q}$$

$$q = r - g.$$

The amount of the mixed colour R in this case is:

$$r = g + q.$$

But by hypothesis r looks the same to the colour-blind eye as g; and since, in general, the amount $q = r - g$ is different from zero, the conclusion is that *the colour-blind eye cannot be sensitive to the colour Q at all.*

The point of intersection of the straight lines that are the loci of points corresponding to colour-mixtures that look alike falls, therefore, at the place of the colour which is missing in the colour sensations of the colour-blind eye.

On YOUNG's hypothesis this colour that is not visible to the colour-blind person is necessarily one of the fundamental colours; for if there were sensation for all the fundamental colours, no other colour sensation composed simply of these fundamental ones could be lacking. Now when we try to discover those colours that look like white (or grey), they will be found to be those which for the normal eye are colours of the hue of the missing fundamental colour or of its complementary colour, mixed with white in different proportions. For all these colours that look like white must lie on a straight line. But every straight line drawn through the point on the chart that corresponds to white contains on its two opposite sides colours of the same hue in different degrees of saturation. But the colours on one half of the line are complementary to those on the other half. Every line of this sort containing colours that all look alike must, however, as just proved, pass through the point where the missing fundamental colour is, and, consequently, must contain on one of its two halves colours of the same hue as the fundamental colour. In the experiments which the writer conducted with Mr. M. it was found that the same appearance as pure grey was produced by a red which corresponded very nearly to the extreme red of the spectrum

in hue (38° of ultramarine and 322° of vermilion), perhaps leaning a little to the purple side, and by a corresponding complementary blue-green (59° ultramarine
and 301° emerald-green). MAXWELL has obtained similar
results, namely, 6 percent ultramarine and 94 percent
vermilion for the red, and 40 percent ultramarine and 60
percent emerald-green for the green. And, besides, as for
normal eyes the red appeared much darker than the grey
and green, with equal luminosity, there can be no more
doubt that it is red, and not green, that is the missing
colour. On YOUNG's hypothesis, therefore, red blindness
would be explained as a paralysis of the red-sensitive
nerves.

If a red not far from the extreme red of the spectrum
is really one of the fundamental colours, the two others
cannot be very far anyhow from the green and violet as
chosen by YOUNG.

The result of this would be that people who are red-
blind are not sensitive except to green and violet and
blue, which is a mixture of the first two. The *red* of the
spectrum which seems to stimulate the green-sensitive
nerves just a little and the violet-sensitive nerves almost
not at all, according to this, would have to appear to red-
blind persons as a *saturated green of low luminosity*, containing appreciable amounts of the other colours mixed
with it. Red of low luminosity which is still adequate to
excite the red-sensitive nerves of the normal eye is, on the
contrary, no longer adequate to excite the green-sensitive
nerves, and therefore this sort of light appears black to
red-blind individuals.

The *yellow* of the spectrum will appear as *brilliant
saturated green*, and doubtless it is just because it does
give the saturated and more luminous shade of this colour
that the red-blind select the name of this colour and
describe all these peculiar hues of green as being yellow.

Green as compared with yellow begins to show an admixture of the other fundamental colours, being therefore indeed a more luminous but yet a pale shade of
green, like that produced by red and yellow. According
to SEEBECK's observations, the most luminous part of
the spectrum for red-blind individuals is, not in the yel-

low as for normal vision, but in the green-blue.[1] As a matter of fact, on the assumption that green stimulates the green-sensitive nerves most, as must be the case, the maximum of the total stimulation for red-blind persons will be rather towards the side of the blue, because here the stimulation of the violet-sensitive nerves increases. What a red-blind individual means by white is naturally a mixture of his two fundamental colours in some definite proportion, which looks green-blue to us; and therefore he regards the transitional shades in the spectrum from green to blue as being grey.

Farther on in the spectrum the second fundamental colour, which a red-blind person calls blue, begins to predominate, because although indigo-blue is still rather pale to him, yet by its luminosity it appears to his eye to be a more striking representative of this colour than violet. Such a one can distinguish the difference of appearance between blue and violet. The subject H. who was examined by SEEBECK knew where the boundary came, but explained that he preferred to call violet *dark blue*. Incidentally, the blue hues must look to the red-blind pretty much as they do to normal persons, because with the latter also there is not much admixture here with red.

All these colours of the spectrum must appear to the red-blind to have certain differences, even if they are less marked. Evidently therefore by paying more attention to them and by practice, they may even learn to call very saturated colours by their right names. But for paler colours the distinctions above mentioned must be too much for them, as they cannot get rid of the confusion.

With respect now to the other group of colour-blind persons comprised in SEEBECK's first division, there are not yet sufficient observations to enable us to define their condition perfectly. According to SEEBECK's data, the difference between them and the red-blind is that they have no difficulty in detecting the transition between violet and red, which to all red-blind persons appears blue. On the other hand, they are confused between green, yellow, blue and red. Both classes confound the

[1] In the yellow-green is more correct.—N.

same hue with green, but individuals of SEEBECK's first class choose a more yellow-green than red-blind persons do. They are not sensitive to the farthest red, and the brightest part of the spectrum for them is in the yellow.[1] They also discriminate only two hues in the spectrum, which they call, probably quite correctly, blue and red. Accordingly, it may be conjectured that their difficulty is due to insensitivity of the green-sensitive nerves, but further investigations on this point are desirable.

Besides total insensitivity, of course, also there may occur all kinds of degrees of lowered sensitivity of the nerves of one sort or the other, with a resultant inability of discriminating colours to a greater or less extent. Cases have also been reported by WILSON and TYNDALL where the trouble was not congenital, but appeared suddenly as a result of serious injuries to the head or eye-strain.

So far as examination of colour-blind persons is concerned, naturally extremely little information can be obtained by asking them how they call this or that colour; for these persons are obliged to use the system of names to describe their sensations which has been devised for the sensations of the normal eye, and which therefore is not adapted for their case. It is not only not adapted because it contains the names of too many hues, but because in the series of colours in the spectrum the differences we speak of are differences of hue, but to colour-blind persons these are merely differences of saturation or of luminosity. Whether what they call yellow and blue corresponds to our yellow and blue, is more than doubtful. Hence, their replies to questions about colours are usually hesitating and perplexed, and seem to us muddled and contradictory.

SEEBECK's method of giving colour-blind persons a selection of coloured papers or worsteds with instructions to arrange them according to their similarity is much better, though still far from satisfactory. But the number of colour tests would have to be enormous in order to include the hues that are characteristic of the difficulty, in their precise admixture with white and of the right

[1] A little towards the orange, about at wave-length 600$\mu\mu$.—N.

luminosity, so that it would be possible to formulate the complete equation for the colour-blind eye. But as long as it is merely a question of similarity, it will be hard to tell whether the difference is one of hue, saturation or luminosity. It is simply by accident, therefore, that a few definite results can be obtained.

On the other hand, the colour top as designed by MAXWELL enables us to obtain quickly the requisite data with great accuracy, because it is easy to make a set of colours by mixture that to the colour-blind eye appear to be *absolutely alike*. Here the chief thing denoting the fundamental character of the trouble is to ascertain what two colours are confused with pure grey as obtained on the colour top by mixing white and black. One of them, which in this case appears comparatively much darker to the colour-blind eye than it does to the normal eye, is the missing fundamental colour. At the same time it will be easy too to discover whether there is still some trace of sensitivity for the missing fundamental colour, or not.

To test the theories here propounded, it will be necessary besides to determine whether every given colour, and especially the principal colours of the spectrum, can be compounded for the colour-blind by mixing two suitably selected colours.

G. WILSON has directed particular attention to the danger for navigation and railways that might be caused by not being able to detect coloured signals on account of colour blindness. He found on the average one colour-blind person in every 17.7 individuals.

4

Principles of a New Theory of the Color Sense

Ewald Hering

We have reached, after an analysis—in my opinion completely without prejudices—of the retinal sensations, the assumption of six simple or basic sensations of which two, namely white and black, have been discussed previously. Now is the time to supplement the theory of the black-white or colorless retinal sensations, previously developed, with a theory of the color sensations. I am herewith reporting the principles of the latter.

The six basic sensations of the optic substance are arranged in three pairs: black and white, blue and yellow, green and red.

Each of these three pairs corresponds to an assimilation and dissimilation process of special quality so that, therefore, the optic substance is capable of the chemical change or metabolism in three different ways.

Assuming the correctness of these premises, two possibilities present themselves. Either the three kinds of the metabolism are mutually dependent or each of them is independent from the other. The latter possibility is not only the simpler one but is in keeping with the facts as far as I can see. Therefore, I can consider the optic substance also as a mixture of three chemically different substances each of which (at least within the limits here under consideration) is able to dissimilate and assimilate independently of the other two. This interpretation simplifies the representation considerably, and only therefore

This selection is taken from Ewald Hering, *Zur Lehre vom Lichtsinne* (Principles of a New Theory of the Color Sense), Vienna, 1878; translated by Kay Butler.

do I prefer it to the others, which basically are perhaps the more correct interpretations, according to which the optic substance represents a whole homogeneous substance being capable, however, of three different kinds of dissimilation and assimilation.

With this reservation I can distinguish three different components of the optic substance which I will designate as the black-white perceiving, the blue-yellow perceiving, and the red-green perceiving substance.

As one speaks in a figurative sense of red, yellow, etc. rays, one can also distinguish the three substances as the black-white, blue-yellow, and red-green, and can oppose the first one to the other two as the *colorless* to the *colored*.

Concerning the black-white substance, now taking the place of the optic substance previously discussed as generally the substance in the fifth report, I have assumed that its dissimilation corresponds to the white and its assimilation to the black; *concerning the blue-yellow and the red-green substance I don't offer any opinion for the time being which color is the D-color and which is the A-color. The three substances do not compose the optic substance in equal parts; on the contrary the black-white substance is contained more plentifully in the organ of vision than the other two, and neither are the other two equal among each other.*

As in the black-white substance, dissimilation and assimilation take place continually at the same time in the other two substances. But according to the different quantity of the three substances, *in general* the dissimilation and assimilation are also much more considerable in the black-white substance than in the other two colored substances, and therefore the weight of the always simultaneously present six basic sensations differs greatly: relatively great of the black and white, very small of the four colored basic sensations.

Therefore, the four color perceptions cross the threshold only under especially favorable circumstances, otherwise they are drowned by the simultaneous black-white perception.

All rays of the visible spectrum have a dissimilating effect on the black-white substance, but the different rays to a different degree. But only certain rays have a dissimilating effect on the blue-yellow or the green-red substance, certain others have an assimilating effect and certain rays none at all. Each of the three substances, so to speak, sees its special spectrum; in the real spectrum these three partial spectrums lie, as it were, over or in each other. The spectrum of the black-white substance is most white or brightest in the "Yellow," and loses brightness in both directions. The spectrum of the blue-yellow substance falls into two parts, one yellow and one blue; both parts are divided by a spot which is lightless for the blue-yellow substance, that is the spot of the pure "Green." The spectrum of the green-red substance falls into three parts, a green middle part, and two red end parts. Accordingly it contains two spots which are lightless for the green-red substance, i.e. the spot of the pure "Yellow" and the pure "Blue." The total spectrum of the optic substance, therefore, has three physiologically distinguished points which are those where except for the white only one basic color is visible, namely the pure yellow, green and blue. The proper red is extremely small in the spectrum since the spectral red contains much yellow.

The first part of the spectrum from red to the pure yellow is, therefore (if we disregard the black and the counter colors of the visible colors which are below the threshold), mixed of white, red and yellow; the second part from pure yellow to green is mixed of white, yellow and green; the third part from green to blue is mixed of white, green and blue; the fourth part, finally, is mixed of white, blue and red. In the pure yellow, green and blue appear only white aside from the corresponding basic color.

Mixed light appears colorless if it creates an equally strong dissimilation and assimilation moment for the blue-yellow as well as for the red-green substance because both moments then cancel each other and the effect on the black-white substance appears clearly.

Two objective kinds of light which together produce white are, therefore, not to be defined as "*complementary*" but as *antagonistic* kinds of light because they do not complete each other into white but only make this appear clearly because as antagonists they mutually make their effect impossible.

Since the size of the dissimilation or assimilation, which is conditioned by a light stimulus in one of the three substances, depends on the intensity of the stimulus as well as on the irritability we have, according to the three substances or qualities of the metabolism in the optic substance, to distinguish between three different kinds of D-irritability as well as A-irritability, thus a total of six different kinds of irritability which we can simply distinguish as the *black, white, green, red, blue, and yellow irritability*.

Each of these six irritabilities is a variable size and, in particular, the D-irritability is by no means always as great as the corresponding A-irritability, on the contrary, the ratio of the two can be quite disparate.

Therefore, not only can the same light mixture appear sometimes lighter and sometimes darker, but also sometimes somehow colored and sometimes colorless depending on the ratio of the present six irritabilities which condition what I want to call the *mood of the organ of vision*.

5

Examination of a Total Color-Blind

Ewald Hering

Through the kindness of my esteemed colleague, Professor Sattler, I had the opportunity to examine a total color-blind who possesses sufficient acuteness of vision and a nearly normal discriminative sensitiveness for brightness necessary for more accurate tests. I had wished for such a case for years because it could, so to speak, be put to the proof. That is, if in the eyes of a color-blind the rays reaching the light-sensitive layer of the retina do not suffer on their way through the eye any essential losses through absorption (in the lens and the Macula Lutea), or because of the fluorescence, other than in a normal eye, and if no other anomalies exist, then, according to the theory of color sense represented by myself, the location of the brightest spot in the spectrum of the color-blind and a substantial shortening at the red end could not only be predicted but it could also be stated how he would see any objective color. Based on that theory one was able to produce in advance for any colored area that white, grey, or black area which to the color-blind would appear like the colored one by type and brightness, and just the same it could be predetermined for each homogenous colored light at what brightness of any other homogenous or white light the color-blind should see these lights without any distinction. In short, one was in the position to produce in advance any number of pairs of exchange colors. If he then

This selection is taken from Ewald Hering, "Examination of a Total Color-Blind" (Untersuchung eines Total Farbenblinden), *Archiv für die Gasammte Physiologie des Menschen und der Thiere*, Bonn, 1891, Nos. XI and XII, pp. 563-564; 603-608; translated by Kay Butler.

really could not distinguish between these, if they seemed the same to him by type and brightness, then this again furnished a conclusive proof for the usefulness of the theory. Based on the theory of Young and Helmholtz, nobody has so far been able to derive even two exchange colors which appear the same to a total colorblind.

As the following will show, the result of the examination corresponded, in a manner even surprising to myself, to everything that had to be expected from the theory. It was confirmed that for the eye of the total color-blind any colored light has that irritability which I have called the white valence of the colored light in connection with the normal eye. Since with a normal eye one is able to measure this white valence of any colored light and to assign the same white valence to a differently colored or white light visibly close by, so for a totally color-blind eye, if no other complications from other disturbances exist, one could in advance form an equation from each two colors, which under normal circumstances seem completely different to us in shade and brightness, by creating the suitable proportion of intensity.

RESULTS FOR THE THEORY OF THE COLOR SENSE

In a little treatise, "On the explanation of the colorblindness from the theory of the complementary colors," [1] I tried to derive from this theory the type of color sensations that would be experienced by the partial color-blind, who were then still called red or green blind. Soon thereafter the known case, reported by v. Hippel, of one-sided partial color-blindness brought proof of the correctness of what was expected from the theory. At that time I was able to derive from the theory in an analogous manner the type of visual sensations of the total color-blind, and to refer to a case, described by Otto Becker,[2] of a nearly total one-sided color-blind which equally answered the requirements of the theory. At that time I did not yet know the course of the curve of the white valences in the spectrum, and I had not as yet developed the methods for the measuring of the white valences of colored lights. After this had happened and I was in the position to

determine with approximate accuracy the white valence
of any colored light, I was able to represent as probable
that two radiations, for us completely different by type
and color, ought to appear the same to a total color-blind
(if in his eye the light rays on their way to the retina
have not suffered any substantial losses through absorp
tion other than in the normal eye) while both show the
same colorless brightness with relatively reduced illumin
ation to a normal eye adapted to darkness; that, further,
the curve of the white valences in the spectrum of the
normal eye will be equal to the so-called brightness curve
of the total color-blind and, also, ought to have a completely different shape from the brightness curve in the
spectrum of the normal eye.[3] The case described here
has now proved the correctness of these expectations, too.

The fact that the three variables of the color sense are
not red, green, and violet (blue) but that they are white-
black, yellow-blue, and red-green results conclusively from
the phenomena of the simultaneous and successive con-
trasts (the so-called fatigue phenomena), from the
changes in the saturations and the shadings of colored
lights when their intensity is greatly reduced or increased,
and from the type of color sense in the peripheral field
of vision, so that for the support of such an assumption
the phenomena of the congenital or acquired color-blindness need not be pointed out. Nevertheless, the experiments which nature has made for us in such cases are of
great interest. Insofar as it may now pass for a test of the
correctness of a hypothesis, enabling us to predict the
results of such experiments of nature, the assumption of
the three aforementioned variables of the color sense has
passed this test. For when I made that assumption there
was no known case of one-sided red-green blindness and
no case of total color-blindness had been examined more
closely.

As is known, it has been attempted to bring the phenomena of total color-blindness into accord with the
theory of Young-Helmholtz. Since there are still adherents of this theory, I want to add from the Three-Color
Hypothesis to the explanation of the total color-blindness.

According to the original version of this theory, as represented by Helmholtz in the first edition of his hand-

book and not quite dropped by him in the second edition, the total color-blindness ought to be explained by the missing of two of the three assumed types of fibres. This explanation has been tried repeatedly although not by Helmholtz himself.

Helmholtz as well as other adherents of the theory has designed so-called curves of the irritability intensity for those three types of fibres; this curve is supposed to depict with its ordinates the relative degree of the irritability, through the various spectral lights, of each type of fibre. In all these curve systems only the curve of the "green perceiving" fibres is, by shape and aspect, remotely similar to the above-mentioned curve of the white valences. One might now be tempted to assume that the latter curve is the true curve of the green perceiving fibres and that the deviations of this curve, which are in parts significant as shown by the alleged green curves of the curve system in question, rest either on wrong hypotheses or observations, or on individual differences. Assuming this, the color-blind K. ought to see the entire spectrum exclusively as green according to Young's theory.

However, the following known facts speak against this:

1. In the case of one-sided, nearly total color-blindness, described by Becker, the affected eye saw everything as colorless but not as green.
2. In cases of acquired one-sided or two-sided total color-blindness (in the entire field of vision or in single parts thereof) everything looks equally colorless and not green.
3. In the periphery of our field of vision we, too, see all colors which do not have too great a saturation or spread, and also white areas, as colorless but not as green.

Since in all these cases the person involved knows the green light sensations as well as the colorless ones, it cannot be assumed that ignorance of the distinction between green and white is the reason for this as it is with congenital color-blindness on both sides.

Added to these known facts is now the one, stated here for the first time, *that the so-called brightness curve in the spectrum of the color-blind is essentially identical with the curve of the white valences in the spectrum of the normal eye.* However, it is impossible to assume that the green-perceiving fibres alone are still irritable in an eye adapted to the dark because then, as the intensity of all colored radiations at increased natural or artificial twilight decreases and the adaptation to the dark sets in, in the same proportion would everything visible pass more and more over into green and, finally, everything in general still clearly visible would have to be seen as green.

Just as our findings about a total color-blind are not compatible with the older version of Young's theory, as discussed above, neither are they compatible with its more recent modification, represented especially by Fick, which has recently been elaborated by Helmholtz without, however, declaring himself positively in favor of it. According to the latter a total color-blind ought to possess, indeed, all three types of fibres with their different specific energies but would not be able to see either green or red or violet because all three types of fibres are supposedly always equally strongly irritated by any colored light; in other words, the "curve for the irritability intensity" is supposedly exactly the same for all three types of fibres. If, according to Young-Helmholtz, white is supposed to be perceived at simultaneous and equally strong irritability of red, green, and violet, then the total color-blind would indeed see everything colored as colorless.

Helmholtz supposes (II Edition, p. 349) that "three types of photochemically decomposable substances are deposited in the end organs of the fibres of the optic nerves which types have a different sensitivity for the different parts of the spectrum." The decrease of the color sense towards the periphery of the retina is supposedly founded on the quality or mixture of those photochemical substances which cause these substances to become progressively more similar and, finally, equal as the distance from the center of the retina becomes greater.

This hypothesis allows the convenience for each retinal zone and for each case of congenital or acquired color-blindness to suppose that change in the nature of the three photochemical substances which seems to be required by the given type of the color sense. Color-blindness now is no longer a pathological deficiency as interpreted by Young and, earlier, by Helmholtz; also, one could not, based on the knowledge of the three primary colors and the normal curves of the irritability intensity, derive from the theory the type of color sense in case one or two fibres of the optic nerve are missing, but one ought to establish for each given case of color-blindness and for each retinal zone a corresponding auxiliary hypothesis about the change of the three photochemical substances. Each case is really not explained by the theory but by the *ad hoc* auxiliary hypothesis made each time.

For one case of color-blindness it might now be assumed that the photochemical substances of all three types of fibres on the retina are the same, and that the curve of the white valences, depicted above, is held in common with the curve of the irritability intensity of all three types of fibres of the color-blind. However, how can it be explained that this curve is identical with the curve of the white valences of the normal eye? No one would want to assume that, with growing twilight or artificial adaptation of our eye to the dark, the three photochemical substances of the fibres of our optical nerves become progressively similar to each other and, finally, almost or completely identical.

The above should suffice; for it can hardly be assumed that one would try to explain the identity of the curve of the white valences of normal eyes and completely color-blind eyes from Young's theory. Even A. *Koenig*, the latest defender of the latter, who ran his experiments in the physics institute headed by Helmholtz himself, was content to find that the "lack of a simple connection" of total color-blindness "to the not pathologically altered color system was of no consequence," [4] and Helmholtz did not even discuss total color-blindness in the second edition of his handbook.

In this handbook (p. 382), Helmholtz remarks on the theory of the color sense represented by myself: "I do not believe that it is necessary in this book to engage in greater detail in such hypothetical opinions." Yet Helmholtz has dedicated a few pages to the theory of the complementary colors and, thus, betrayed sufficiently that he did not engage in it in greater detail himself. With respect to the content of the present treatise only the following sentence will be stressed as proof: "Mr. Hering identifies the sensation of brightness with the sensation of white. He, therefore, asserts logically that no sensation of brightness is connected with the sensation of pure blue or yellow." This account is altogether incorrect. Rather, at that time I used not less than six (paragraphs 40 and 41) of the 34 pages of my sketch of a theory of the color sense exclusively in order to explain in what way the colored components of a visual sensation, i.e., the pure, thought of as completely isolated, sensation of yellow, blue, red, and green co-determine the brightness of the total sensation. On p. 114 I stated explicitly that a "medium brightness or darkness," comparable to a medium grey, belongs to these colored components; and it is further explained in detail in what cases the brightness of a colorless normal sensation ought to be increased or decreased by the addition of a colored component. Helmholtz has remained ignorant of all this. The theory of the complementary colors ought to a great extent to have been unintelligible to him for that reason; for the assumption that the brightness of a colored light sensation is determined not only by its colored but also by its colorless components is one of the bases of the entire theory, another reason why I devoted more than the sixth part of the entire treatise to the discussion of it. If I was then still of the opinion that the same medium brightness or darkness had to be attributed to all 4 (thought of as absolutely isolated from the colorless sensation) basic colors, and recognized only later that these four basic colors determine in different ways the brightness of the total sensation, this does not alter the fact that from the beginning I attributed an equally substantial influence on the brightness of the total sensation to the colored as well as the colorless components of the sensation.

Other erroneous facts that Mr. Helmholtz mentions in other places about the theory represented by myself have no relation to the content of the present treatise and will be examined at another opportunity.

REFERENCES

1. Lotos, Vol. 1, 1880.
2. *Archiv f. Opthalmologie*, Vol. XXV, 2, 1879, p. 205.
3. *Dieses Archiv*, Vol. XL, P. 19, 1887.
4. "Die Grundempfindungen und ihre Intensitaets-Vertheilung im Spectrum," *Sitzungsber. d. Berliner Akad.*, 29 July 1886.

6

Color Blindness

ADOLPH FICK

*Editor's Note: In its classic form, the Young-Helmholtz
theory had great difficulty in explaining color-blindness. If
we see white only when there is a combination of red,
green, and blue then how can we see white if one of these
primaries is missing? In this article Fick advances a hypothesis that has been used by all advocates of the Young
theory in order to get over this difficulty.*

The diversity of the color sensations mentioned in the
previous paragraphs exists only if a stimulation of the
elements in the polar zones of the retina is involved. As
soon as the stimulated element is only a few millimeters
away from the fovea centralis it is then, in general, not
capable of such a diversity of different sensations. Only
two colors, yellow and blue, can be distinquished, and
the diversity of all possible sensations of light is reduced
to the shadings of yellow from the more saturated through
the paler shades to white and from there through paler
shadings of blue to the more saturated blue, and in the
area of this diversity there is—which must be emphasized
especially—absolutely no continuous transition feasible
from a yellow to a blue shading that would not go
through white. The diversity, therefore, is a single infinite
one and could be depicted graphically by a line without
any expansion in the second dimension.

All radiations, whether homogeneous or mixed, producing the impression of red, yellow, or green at the

This selection has been taken from Adolf Fick, *Handbuch
des Physiologie*, Vol. III "Handbuch der Physiologie der Sinnesorgane," Part II, "Die Lehre von der Lichtempfindung,"
Chapter 4, "The Mixed Colors," pp. 206-210, translated by
Kay Butler.

pole create the impression of yellow in the zone in question and, indeed, the paler the radiation the greener will the impression be at the polar zone. All radiations which here produce the impression of blue or violet create the impression of blue at the outer zone and, again, the paler the radiation is, the closer to green the impression appears at the polar zone. Radiations which give the impression of blue-green at the polar zone look white at the outer zone.

Places of the retina located laterally farther away do not offer any qualitative differences of the light impressions. Every stimulation of them leads to the sensation of white, and only quantitative differences in it are possible.

The limits of these three retinal zones are not very sharp, rather the double infinite color diversity of the polar zone contracts gradually, but rather fast, into the single infinite one at the middle, and this one gradually into a zone of indistinquishability at the border zone. Very remarkable is also the fact that the distension of the zones is dependent upon various color discriminabilities, upon the size of the retinal image of the color object. That is, the larger the retinal image of the colored object, the farther away laterally can the colors be completely or partly perceived. With an exceedingly small retinal image no color can be distinguished even with the polar zone of the retina as was mentioned earlier. Leaving these difficulties aside for the time being, Young's theory too can easily answer for the imperfect color sense of the side parts of the retina.

It seems that for this purpose the following hypothesis[1] could most naturally be made. The three specific, differently perceiving types of fibres are distributed evenly on the retina but their end apparatuses alter their irritability for different radiations if one goes from the fovea centralis to the side, and that in the sense that the differences in the irritability, which one type of end apparatus shows for various radiations, are equalized more and more and, also, that the differences in the irritability of the three types of end apparatuses become progressively smaller for the same kind of rays. These latter differences—this we have to assume especially—have already disappeared completely in the middle zone for the end apparatuses of the red- and green-perceiving rays.

The three irritability curves for homogeneous rays projected in the way they have been drawn up in Fig. 1 for the polar zone would, accordingly, for the middle zone show about the shape of the three curves RGB in Fig. 1. The curves R and G really coincide exactly and a dotted line has been drawn up alongside the solid one only for clarity's sake. For the border zone all three curves coincide into one straight line parallel to the abscissa axis. Here it might well be emphasized again that in constructing the curves, the different radiations

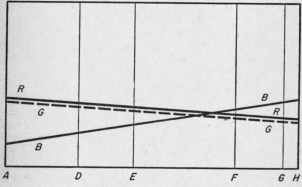

Fig. 1.

have to be thought of as certain intensities so that the total physiological impression has the same intensity. The objective energy of the least refrangible and the most refrangible radiations must, therefore, be thought of as much greater than that of the radiations of medium refrangibility.

It is noteworthy that the irritability through light is not at all less at the side parts of the retina than in the yellow spot, as one might perhaps assume according to the other imperfections of the side parts. They rather seem to be superior to the yellow spot as far as the irritability is concerned. This has earlier been asserted frequently, and has recently been proved beyond a doubt through exact tests by Schadow.[2] He found that an object with lower light intensity is more easily visible 30° lateral from the fixation direction than in it. An object situated 60° laterally from it, however, must light more intensely in order to be perceived than it has to if it lies in the fixation direction. It is conceivable, though, that the irritability of the retina even in this far outer zone is still as great or greater than in the yellow spot, and that the invisibility of evenly strong shining objects throwing their images there stems only from the fact that these images themselves are less illuminated because the bundles of rays going to their points have less of an opening on account of the slanted passage.

A considerable fraction of all people (probably more than 1/20) have a retina the polar zone of which does not even possess the above-mentioned diversity of color sensations. Such individuals are called color-blind. The diversity of their color sensations is more or less great. It is probable that this condition consists simply of the fact that the change in the quality of the retina, which in the normal eye begins only in a certain middle zone, in the color-blind eye already takes place in the fovea centralis. The degree of the color-blindness could be called so much greater as a farther outward lying zone of the retina of the normal eye corresponds in quality to the fovea centralis of the color-blind eye. The total color-blindness would consist of the entire retina possessing the quality of the outermost border zone of the normal eye.

There seems to exist a partial abnormal color-blindness which is distinguished in type from the middle zone of the normal eye. This could be explained by the fact that a pair of irritability curves of 3 types of fibres becomes congruent different from the pair for the green- and red-perceiving fibres, which fact would then lead to another system of color sensations. However, since this entire subject pertains to the pathology rather than the physiology of the eye this is not the place to enter into the details of these complicated phenomena which in part have not as yet been completely clarified.

The adherents of Young's theory of color sensation have earlier tried to explain in a different manner the abnormal as well as the normal color-blindness of the outer parts of the retina. They supposed that where the color system is based on a single infinite diversity, one type of fibre, e.g. the red-perceiving, is missing. However, a part of the retina possessing only blue- and green-perceiving fibres would not be capable of the sensation of white at all. If it is a question of an unknown pathologically color-blind eye, it cannot be determined, of course, whether it possesses the sensation of white because it would not know it as such. With the color-blindness of the middle zone of the normal eye such a subterfuge is not possible since it knows the sensation of white very well from the polar zone of its retina. This opinion can be refuted even more strikingly by the fact that the radiations which create the impression of green at the polar zone, create the impression of yellow at the middle zone although it is exactly here that the irritation of the green-perceiving fibres should stand out undisturbed by the irritation of the red-perceiving ones; the radiation in question, therefore, ought to look decidedly greener at the polar zone than it does on places of the retina provided with red-perceiving fibre ends.

In any event, one could invalidate these arguments with the assertion that one would not be entitled to compare directly the qualitative character of the color sensations on widely separate places of the retina. Therefore, I want at least to point out another consideration from which, it seems to me, results with great probability the assumption that the absence of one or two types of fibres can never explain the reduction of the diversity of fibres on the outer zones of the retina. As mentioned above, the transition from the double infinite diversity at the polar zone to the single infinite one at the middle zone is gradual. One should, therefore, assume that the irritability of the red-perceiving fibres lessens from zone to zone until it finally reaches zero, in other words, until the red-perceiving fibres are missing. This decrease in the irritability of the red-perceiving fibres, however, should obviously happen the fastest with the least refrangible kinds of rays since their color impression changes the fastest going from the polar zone to the side parts of the retina. If one constructs the irritability curves of the

three types of fibres for all these zones, there would probably be one zone where the irritability curve of the red-
perceiving fibres would run almost similar to that of the
green-perceiving one. For this zone, however, the color
area would be reduced to a length of a line going from B,
Fig. 2, to a point which would divide the side RG pro-
portionately to the ordinates of the irritability curves R
and G where, therefore, the diversity of the colors would

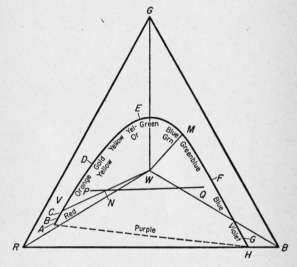

Fig. 2.

be single infinite similar to the one described above.
Then, with a still further decrease of the irritability in
the red-perceiving fibres, a double infinite diversity of
color sensations would appear again corresponding to an
area located in the triangle above the aforementioned
line. This would be the case on such zones of the retina
where the irritability of the red-perceiving fibres would
certainly have become less but where the ordinates of
the curve would not be proportionate to the ordinates of
the curve representing the green-perceiving fibres. In the
end, the entire color area would naturally retreat to line

BG of the figure. Therefore, between two retinal zones with single infinite color diversity there ought to be enclosed one with a double infinite diversity. However, nothing of this zone has been observed.

The imperfect ability of the side parts of the retina to distinguish colors has in recent times been the subject of tests by numerous researchers[3] whose results have in part been included in this presentation.

REFERENCES

1. *Fick,* Zur Theorie der Farbenblindheit. Arbeiten aus dem physiologischen Laboratorium der Würzburger Hochschule. IV. Lieferung. S.213 Würzburg, 1878. Sep.-Abdr. aus den Verhandlungen der phys.-med. Gesellschaft.
2. *Schadow,* Arch. f.d.ges.Physiol.XIX. S. 499.
3. *Schelske,* Arch. f. Ophthalmologie IX. S.3; *Schön,* Die Lehre vom Gesichtsfelde und seinen Anomalieen. Berlin, 1874; *Klug,* Ueber Farbenempfindung bei indirektem Sehen. f. Ophthalmologie XXI, S.1; *Holmgren,* De la cecite des couleurs etc. Stockholm.

7

A New Theory of Light-Sensation

CHRISTINE LADD-FRANKLIN

The reasons which make it impossible for most people to accept either the Hering or the Young-Helmholtz theories of light sensation are familiar to everyone. The following are the most important of them:—

The Young-Helmholtz theory requires us to believe: (*a*) something which is strongly contradicted by consciousness, viz. that the *sensation* white is nothing but an even mixture of red-green-blue *sensations*; (*b*) something which has a strong antecedent improbability against it, viz. that under certain definite circumstances (e.g. for very ex-centric parts of the retina and for the totally color-blind) all three color-sensations are produced in exactly their original integrity, but yet that they are never produced in any other than that *even* mixture which gives us the sensation of white; (*c*) something which is quantitatively quite impossible, viz. that after-images, which are frequently very brilliant, are due to nothing but what is left over in the self-light of the retina after part of it has been exhausted by fatigue, although anyone can see that the *whole* of the self-light is excessively faint.

The theory of Hering avoids all of these difficulties of the Young-Helmholtz theory, but at the cost of introducing others which are equally disagreeable; it sins against the first principles of the physiologist by requiring us to think that the process of building up highly organized animal tissue is useful in giving us knowledge of the

This selection is taken from the book by Christine Ladd-Franklin, *Colour and Colour Theories*, New York: Harcourt, Brace and Co., 1929, pp. 66-71. Reprinted by permission of Harcourt, Brace and Company, Inc.

external world instead of supposing that it takes place (as in every other instance known to us) simply for the sake of its future useful tearing down; it necessarily brings with it a quite hopeless confusion between our ideas of the *brightness* and the *relative whiteness* of a given sensation (as is proved by the fact that it enables Hering to rediscover, under the name of the specific brightness of the different colors, a phenomenon which has long been perfectly well known as the Purkinje phenomenon); the theory is contradicted (at least the present conception of it) by the following (new) fact—the white made out of R and BG is *not the same thing* as the white made out of blue and yellow; for if (being mixed on the color-wheel) these two whites are made equally bright at an ordinary intensity, they will be found to be of very different brightness when the illumination is made very faint.

Nevertheless, the theory of Hering would have to be accepted, if it were the only possible way of escape from the difficulties of the Young-Helmholtz theory. But these difficulties may be met by a theory which has the following for its principal assumptions.

In its earliest stage of development, vision consisted of nothing but a sensation of grey (if we use the word grey to cover the whole series black-grey-white). This sensation of grey was brought about by the action upon the nerve-ends of a certain chemical substance, set free in the retina under the influence of light. In the course of development of the visual sense, the molecule to be chemically decomposed became so differentiated as to be capable of losing only a part of its exciting substance at once; three chemical constituents of the exciter of the grey-sensation can therefore now be present separately (under the influence of three different parts of the spectrum respectively), and they severally cause the sensations of red, green, and blue. But when all three of these substances are present at once, they recombine to produce the exciter of the grey sensation, and thus it happens that the objective mixing of three colors, in proper proportions, gives a sensation of no *color* at all, but only white.

This theory is found, upon working it out in detail,

to avoid the difficulties of the theories of Helmholtz and of Hering.

Its assumption of a separate chemical process for the production of the sensation of grey gives it the same great advantage over the Young-Helmholtz theory that is possessed by the theory of Hering; it enables it, namely, to account for the remarkable fact that the sensation of grey exists unaccompanied by any sensation whatever of color under the five following sets of circumstances— when the portion of the retina affected is very small, when it is very far from the fovea, when the illumination is very faint, when it is very intense, and when the retina is that of a person who is totally color-blind. This advantage my theory attains by the perfectly natural and simple assumption of a *partial* decomposition of chemical molecules; that of Hering requires us to suppose that sensations so closely related as red and green are the accompaniments of chemical processes so dissimilar as the building up and the tearing down of photo-chemical substances, and farther that two complementary colors call forth photo-chemical processes which destroy each other, instead of combining to produce the process which underlies the sensation of grey.

Of the first four of the above enumerated cases, the explanation will readily suggest itself; in the case of the totally color-blind it is simply that that differentiation of the primitive molecules by which they have become capable of losing only a part of their exciting substance at one time has not taken place; the condition, in other words, is a condition of atavism. In partial color-blindness, and in the intermediate zones of the retina in normal vision, the only colors perceived are yellow and blue. This would indicate that the substance which in its primitive condition excites the sensation of grey becomes in the first place differentiated into two substances, the exciters of yellow and blue respectively, and that at a later stage of development the exciter of the sensation of yellow becomes again separated into two substances which produce respectively the sensations of red and of green. In this way the unitary (non-mixed) character of the sensation yellow is accounted for by a three-color theory as completely as by a four-color theory. A three-color theory is rendered a necessity by the fact that it alone is reconcilable with the results of König's experiments for the determination of the color-equations of color-blind and of normal eyes,[1] experiments which far exceed in accuracy any which have yet been made in color-vision, but which owing to the intricate character of the theoretical deductions made from them, have not hitherto been allowed their due weight in the estimation of color-theories.

The explanations which the theory of Hering give of after-images and of simultaneous contrast are not explanations at all, but merely translations of the facts into the language of his theory. My theory is able to deal with them more satisfactorily; when red light, say, has been acting upon the retina for some time, many of the photo-chemical molecules have lost that one of their constituents which is the exciter of the red sensation; but in this mutilated condition they are exceedingly unstable, and their other two constituents (the exciters of the sensations of blue and of green) are gradually set free; the effect of this is that, while the eyes are still open a blue-green sensation is added to the red sensation with the result of making it gradually fade out into white, and, if the eyes are closed, the cause of the blue-green sensation persists until all the molecules affected are totally decomposed. Thus the actual course of the sensation produced by looking at a red object—its gradual fading out, in case of careful fixation, and the appearance of the complementary color if the illumination is diminished or if the eyes are closed—is exactly what the original assumption of a partial decomposition of molecules would require us to predict. The well-known extreme rapidity of the circulation in the retina would make it impossible that the partly decomposed molecules just referred to should remain within the boundaries of the portion of the retina in which they are first produced; and their completed decomposition after they have passed beyond these boundaries is the cause of the complementary color-sensation which we call simultaneous con-

[1] A. König und C. Dieterici, *Sitzungberichte der Berl. Akad.*, 29 Juli, 1886.

trast.[1] The spreading of the actual color which succeeds it would then be accounted for, as Helmholtz suggests, by a diffusion of the colored light in the various media of the eye.

No effort has hitherto been made to explain a very remarkable feature in the structure of the retina—the fact that the retinal elements are of two different kinds, which we distinguish as rods and cones. But this structure becomes quite what one might expect, if we suppose that the rods contain the undeveloped molecules which give us the sensation of grey only, while the cones contain the color molecules, which cause sensations of grey and of color both. The distribution of the rods and cones corresponds exactly with the distribution of sensitiveness to just perceptible light and color excitations as determined by the very careful experiments of Eugen Fick.[2]

Two other theories of light sensation have been proposed, besides the one which I have here outlined, either one of which meets the requirements of a possible theory far better than that of Hering or of Helmholtz; they are those of Göller[3] and Donders.[4] The former is a physical theory. That of Donders is a chemical theory, and very similar to the one which I here propose. Every chemical theory supposes a tearing down of highly complex molecules; Donders' theory supposes in addition that the tearing down in question can take place in two successive stages. But Donders' theory is necessarily a four-color theory; and Donders himself, although the experiments of König above referred to had not at that time been made, was so strongly convinced of the necessity of a three-color theory for the explanation of some of the facts of color-vision that he supplemented his four-process theory in the retina with a three-process theory in the higher centres. The desirableness, therefore,

[1] But see p. 146 n.
[2] "Studien über Licht und Farbenempfindung," *Pflüger's Archiv.*, Bd. xliv, pp. 441, 1888.
[3] "Die Analyse der Lichtwellen durch das Auge," *Du Bois-Reymond's Archiv*, 1889.
[4] "Noch einmal die Farben-systeme," *Gräfe's Archiv. für Ophthalmologie*, Bd. 39 (1), 1884.

of devising a partial decomposition of molecules *of such a nature* that the fundamental color-processes assumed can be three in number instead of four is apparent.

But the theory of Donders is open to a still graver objection. The molecules assumed by him must, in order to be capable of four different semi-dissociations, consist of at least eight different atoms or groups of atoms. The red-green dissociations and the yellow-blue dissociations we may then represent symbolically by these two diagrams respectively:—

But it will be observed that the two completed dissociations end by having set free *different* combinations; in the one case 1 is combined with 2 and in the other case 1 is combined with 8, etc. If, now, the partial dissociations are so unlike as to cause sensations of yellow and blue (or of red and green) it is not probable that completed dissociations which end in setting free *different* chemical combinations should produce the *same* sensation, grey. The difficulty introduced by Donders' theory is therefore (as in the case of Hering's theory) as great as the difficulty sought to be removed. It is the desire to secure the advantages of a partial dissociation theory, without the disadvantages of the theory of Donders that has led me to devise a partial dissociation of molecules of a different kind.

8

Bearing of Results on Theories of Color-Vision

MARY COLLINS

It is not proposed in this section to assert dogmatically that the results fit in with any particular theory. It was explained in the Introduction that the experiments were carried out without any preconceived theory causing a bias, and the question now arises, how far do the results tell for or against existing theories?

Although we have considerable admiration for Dr Edridge-Green's practical achievements, which have been productive of much valuable information and many useful tests, it must be admitted that his theory of color-vision is difficult to reconcile with facts. It has been found impossible to group the ten subjects into specific unit classes. *H* and *J* may be grouped as two-units, although we should be very loath to admit that red and violet are the two colors visible to them. It somewhat disarms criticism to find that, according to Edridge-Green, they are not supposed to see these two colors, but only the centres of their two psycho-physical units which are yellow and blue. Even admitting this, subject *J* raises a difficulty. He appears an extreme case of red-green color-blindness with his yellow and blue sensations reduced in sensitivity. In fact, he may be regarded as akin to, or as just preceding monochromatic vision. If so, and

This selection is taken from the book *Colour Blindness* by Mary Collins (Harcourt, Brace and Company, New York, 1925, pp. 215-220), in which the author records her extensive study of color-blindness. The selection quoted concerns the way in which the various theories of color stand up in explaining her results. Reprinted by permission of Harcourt, Brace and Company, Inc.

if Edridge-Green's theory is understood correctly, should not red and violet, the two extremes of the spectrum, be the colors visible to J? Further, if the centre colors of the units are always the colors seen, then the color sensations of the color-blind must vary from individual to individual, since the position of their psycho-physical units varies. In fact, a shortening of the spectrum at either end will narrow the band of color and shift the centre. J has shortened spectrum at the red end, a large neutral band, a small region of yellow, a second neutral band, a small region of blue, and the violet end shortened. There is no suggestion whatsoever that red and violet are the colors he sees, and certainly yellow does not form the centre of his red, nor blue the centre of his violet. It seems quite clear that yellow and blue are the two colors seen, and that these colors are the last seen before monochromatic vision supervenes.

When we come to the three-units, the same difficulty arises. We find that reddish-green is a term used by the three-unit; therefore, we try to place B in the three-unit class, from that and other evidence, but without success. The three colors of the three-unit class are red, green, and violet. The three-unit never confuses red with green, but is always in difficulty with yellows and blues. This seems contrary to fact. B, or any of the other subjects examined, is always confusing red with green, but yellow and blue are two of his clearest sensations. The confusion of brown with green is a diagnostic sign of the four-unit. This class can see clearly red, yellow, green, and violet, but here again the facts point to different conclusions. The results, therefore, as we have found them, are difficult to reconcile with this theory, and rather appear to give direct evidence against it.

As a further point of explanation, it may be argued that yellow and blue are not clearly seen by the three-unit, that yellow is frequently confused with green, and blue with violet, as Edridge-Green affirms. This is true, but it appears to be a begging of the question. Yellow is confused with green in cases where the green element is absent, as in a compound of yellow-green, or in cases of color-blindness where green has been replaced by yellow and called green by convention, but that does not alter the statement that yellow is a distinct color sensation. Blue, likewise, shows confusion with violet and with pink, but is not that because the red element is not recognized in these two cases. It does not affect the validity of the statement that blue is a clear color sensation of the red-green color-blind.

In the Ladd-Franklin theory, the red element "falls out" in red-blindness, and green is replaced by yellow; in green-blindness the green element "falls out" and yellow replaces red.

In the results submitted, certain cases seem partially to support this theory; whether they wholly support it is difficult to decide. One fact, which does give it support in the extreme cases, is that yellow and blue are the only two colors visible. In H and J's cases the red and green must both have fallen out and been replaced by yellow; in other words, there has been a total regression to the second stage.

It seems more difficult to account for the milder forms. With some of the examinees green is replaced by yellow, which would appear to support the theory; this occurs in cases of red-blindness or in those cases in which the spectrum is shortened. But we have repeatedly shown that red is not totally invisible, nor green either. Therefore, all the red cannot have "fallen out," nor all the green been replaced by yellow.

In green-blindness, the green sensation is said to be missing, and yellow vision takes the place of the red. The same argument holds here, for the red is not always replaced by yellow, nor does the green element always appear to be missing. In fact, the division of color-blinds into two such groups seems unnatural and essentially artificial.[1] There is little difference between a case of shortened spectrum and a case in which the spectrum is of normal length when milder forms of the defect are in question. For in our results there seems little difference between A and B, although the former is credited with a shortening of the spectrum. It may be that Dr. Ladd-Franklin has modified her theory to explain such cases,

---

[1] Dr. Houston's results, of which the writer has just become aware, confirm this statement.

but so far attempts to find a reference to such modification have failed.

The "old" explanation of Helmholtz may be set aside, for the newer explanation fits the facts much better. It must be admitted that few text-books on the subject seem to recognize or acknowledge this second mode of explanation, and still give Helmholtz's views along the line which he himself so vigorously repudiated.

In red-blindness—that is, in cases of shortened spectrum—the red substance has become equal to the green substance; but yellow and blue are the two colors visible. The yellow begins in the orange, and the blue-green forms the neutral band. In green-blindness, the opposite condition occurs, and the neutral band appears in the green.

This theory, while accounting for some of the facts, seems again to make an unnatural division between color-blinds and not to make any allowance for the type of case we have been describing, or those described by Professor Hayes. Even McDougall's modification seems to fail to account for these red-green color-blind cases in which these two colors may sometimes be recognized. If color-blindness is atavistic, and facts seem to confirm that hypothesis, these cases may be regarded as midway between normal vision and total reversion to the blue-yellow stage. The great point of superiority of Edridge-Green's theory is that he recognizes such transitional cases.

Helmholtz's theory admirably fits the facts for extreme cases, those cases in which blue and yellow are the color sensations experienced. It also gives a satisfactory reason why the neutral band should lie in the blue-green in red-blindness and in the green in green-blindness. Yet subjects H and J, as far as we were able to discover, appeared to have a neutral band embracing both. They are neither red-blind nor green-blind, but are red-green blind. It does not seem, however, to explain the milder cases of partial color-blindness, unless it may be possible to account for them along the lines of Peddie by the formation of some derived color triangle which will conform to the facts.

The Hering theory exposes itself to the same objection,

namely, that it explains solely the limiting cases. It has the apparent advantage that red-green blindness is treated as a whole and is not so artificially divided into the types of Helmholtz. The variations, which do undoubtedly exist in this defect, are accounted for by differences in the pigmentation of the eye, and Hering decided, on the basis of experimental results, that color-blinds could be regarded as yellow-sighted or blue-sighted. We have little evidence in favour of, or against, this view.

One outstanding result which does support the Hering theory is that the position of the neutral bands of the color-blinds corresponds with the fundamental colors adopted in the theory. The one neutral band lies in the blue-green which is the green of the Hering theory; the other lies in the complementary of that green, in the purples, which is the red employed by Hering—a red beyond the red end of the spectrum. These facts lend strong support to the theory in the fundamental colors chosen, for if the substances for these two elementary colors are absent, then the color sense must be deficient in red and green, leaving as clear sensations the other two fundamental colors, blue and yellow.

Finally, our tentative finding is that the Hering theory, the Young-Helmholtz theory, and the Ladd-Franklin theory all fit the facts of red-green color-blindness when the defect takes an extreme form, but they seem to fail to take account of cases which suffer from this disability in a less marked degree.

Part II

9

The Development of Thomas Young's Theory of Color Vision

SELIG HECHT

. THOMAS YOUNG'S FUNDAMENTAL CONTRIBUTION

It has been known for a good deal over a hundred ears that the sensation produced by nearly any given ight may be reproduced by the mixture in proper proportions of the light from three selected portions of the pectrum. More generally, and perhaps more accurately tated, all color sensations produced by light may be lescribed in terms of three properly chosen variables. Ine may say

$$L = pA + qB + rC \qquad (1)$$

n which L is the light, A, B, and C are the chosen variables, usually spoken of as primaries, and p, q, and r, are he coefficients representing the respective amounts of he primaries required to match the sensation produced by the light. The particular specifications of these primaries may vary, and indeed may be quite arbitrarily issumed. Nevertheless, they are adequate as a formal lescription of the properties of color vision insofar as hey relate to color mixing.

Such a basic fact should obviously be utilized and incorporated into any mechanism proposed as a theoretical

This selection originally appeared in the *Journal* of the Optical Society of America, 20, No. 5, May 1930, pp. 231-270.

The greater part of this paper was given as an address at he Thomas Young Memorial Meeting of the Optical Society of America, held on October 24th, 1929, at Cornell University, Ithaca, to commemorate the centenary of the death of Thomas Young. Reprinted by permission.

basis for color vision. This indeed was first done about 130 years ago by Thomas Young, the centenary of whose death we are today commemorating. Young[43] supposed that there are three kinds of fibers in the retina, each producing a characteristic sensation, one of red, another of green, and a third of violet (or blue). Each type of fiber is sensitive practically to the whole visible spectrum, but the first possesses a maximum of sensibility in the red, the second in the green, and the third in the blue. Various color sensations then result from the relative strength with which the three different fibers are stimulated by the objective light.

Newton[33] had supposed that certain elements in the retina vibrated in unison with the incident light, and that the "harmony and discord of colors arise from the proportion of the vibrations propagated through the fibers of the optic nerve into the brain as the harmony and discord of sound arise from the proportions of the vibrations of the air."

This conception was not acceptable to Thomas Young. In his famous Bakerian lecture to the Royal Society in 1801 he therefore suggested that since "it is almost impossible to conceive each sensitive point on the retina to contain an infinite number of particles each capable of vibrating in perfect unison with every possible undulation, it becomes necessary to suppose the number limited, for instance, to the three principal colors, red, yellow, and blue, of which the undulations are related in magnitude nearly as the numbers 8, 7, and 6; and that each of the particles is capable of being put in motion less or more forcibly by undulations differing less or more from a perfect unison; for instance, the undulations of green light being nearly in the ratio of 6½ will affect equally the particles in unison with yellow and blue and produce the same effect as a light composed of those two species; and each sensitive filament of the nerve may consist of three portions, one for each principal color." In a later communication, due to the erroneous observations of Wollaston, Young[31] suggested that these basic color sensations are red, green, and violet.

Young does not specifically say that the sensation of

hite is produced by the simultaneous stimulation of the
three fibers. However, it is apparent that this is an obvious
onclusion from his theory. Koenig[22] has pointed out that
Thomas Young rests his theory on a principle which we
in physiology at the present time recognize but which at
that time had not yet been enunciated by its author,
Johannes Müller.[32] This is the principle of the specific
energies of nerves which supposes that no matter how a
given nerve fiber is stimulated, it always produces a certain "energy" or quality which is associated with it. In
this case a specific fiber will produce the sensation of red,
or of green, or of blue depending upon its own self only
and not upon the particular wave length which is used in
stimulating it.

It is not usually recognized that Thomas Young's insight into the problem of color vision went even deeper
than this. He suggested that the color confusions which
were made by his contemporary, Dalton, were due to the
lack or paralysis of those fibers in the retina which were
concerned with the red sensation.

For nearly fifty years these ideas lay buried. They were
rescued from oblivion by Maxwell [30] and by Helmholtz[14]
almost at the same time. It would be difficult to find a
better statement of the position in the history of science
of this theory and of Thomas Young's work in general
than the one given by Helmholtz in his Popular Scientific
Lectures.[15] Helmholtz after describing various aspects of
color vision says: "The nature of colors with all these
marvelous and complicated relations was a riddle which
Goethe in vain attempted to solve; nor were we physicists
and physiologists more successful. I include myself in the
number for I long worked at the task without getting any
nearer my object until I discovered that a wonderfully
simple solution had been made at the beginning of this
century and had been in print ever since for anyone to
read who chose. This solution was found and published by
the same Thomas Young who first showed the correct
method of interpreting the Egyptian hieroglyphics. He
was one of the most acute men who ever lived, but he
had the misfortune to be born far in advance of his con-
temporaries. They looked on him with astonishment but

they could not follow his bold speculations. And so a mass of his most important thoughts remained buried and forgotten in the Philosophical Transactions of the Royal Society until a later generation slowly arrived at the rediscovery of his discoveries and came to appreciate the force of his argument and the accuracy of his conclusions."

II. THE ADEQUACY OF YOUNG'S IDEA

Few among us today suppose that Young's idea as here given in its simple form or as elaborated by Helmholtz,[14] Koenig,[22] von Kries,[27] and others, is adequate as a *complete* theory for the mechanism of color vision. We know very definitely that it is not. The question, however, has often been raised as to whether it can serve even as the basis for a theory of color vision. This question was raised by Aubert,[3] and by Hering[17] almost immediately after Maxwell and Helmholtz first brought Young's idea to light. Aubert, Hering, and more recently Ladd-Franklin[28] considered the problem of color theory from a totally different point of view than did Young. Instead of relying on the objective facts of color mixtures which state that three variables are enough to describe color sensation, these investigators started from their own sensations of color. Perhaps the simplest way of indicating their point of view is to consider the sensations of yellow and white. Mixtures of green and blue lights give a continuous series of colors, the blue-greens, in which both colors are identifiable. The same is true with mixtures of red and blue lights; these give a series of violets and purples in which one can see the two components. But in mixtures of red and green, a new sensation, yellow, arises which contains neither red nor green. Yellow seems to be something by itself. It is definitely not red plus green; and we recognize this by saying that a color is greenish yellow or reddish yellow, not greenish red nor reddish green. The same is true for mixtures of yellow and blue or of green, red, and blue which give white, a totally new sensation.

If Young's idea is correct then it must be supposed that

yellow is a central phenomenon occurring in the brain when in the retina the red and green receiving fibers function simultaneously; similarly, white is the sensation which occurs in the brain when all three receiving fibers, the red, the green, and the blue, function in the retina. It is precisely against such a formulation that Aubert, Hering, and Ladd-Franklin ranged themselves. And as a result first Aubert, then Hering, and later, Ladd-Franklin devised theories which take into consideration the curious uniqueness of the yellow and the white sensations.

One must not minimize the difference between these two positions. It would perhaps be difficult to do so because the work of the last fifty years in color vision has had its origins mainly in the antagonism which has existed between those who, like Helmholtz, Koenig, von Kries, Abney, and others, have accepted and amplified Young's original formulation and those who, like Hering, Aubert, and Ladd-Franklin, have held opposing views. Nevertheless, it is important to remember that these two sets of views are not necessarily antagonistic when, as suggested by v. Kries, they are considered as partial descriptions of different parts of the process of color vision as a whole. It is only when they are concerned with a formulation of the *receptor* process in the retina that the two views are in sharp contrast. And here their differences demand an experimental test.

If there is to be developed an adequate theory for the mechanism of color vision a decision must be made in the very beginning as to which of the two conceptions of yellow and white is correct. Are there special substances or processes in the retina for the reception of yellow and white or are yellow and white phenomena which arise in the brain out of the impulses coming from the three kinds of fibers or processes in the retina? Is a three receptor notion adequate or do we need to have a four or perhaps a five receptor system to account for color vision. Since the data of color mixing may be adequately described on a three dimensional basis they can be described on a four dimensional basis as well—a fact which has been frequently pointed out.[5,13,34,37] The problem is, therefore, essentially a physiological one, and not a mathematical one.

If red light and green light fall on a given retinal area of one eye and a yellow sensation results, it is not possible to decide whether this is the result of a stimulation of two receptors or of one receptor. But if red light falls on the retina of one eye, and green light falls on the corresponding portion of the retina of the other eye, and the result is a yellow sensation, then only Young's idea is tenable, because there must be two receptors involved in making the yellow sensation from red and green. This is precisely what happens in the binocular mixing of colors.

The binocular mixing of colors is an old story. Curiously enough, Helmholtz was unable to fuse colors binocularly and the weight of his authority prevented the binocular fusion of colors from a proper acceptance. Nevertheless, Hering and a number of other investigators showed precisely what was wrong with Helmholtz' experiments and arranged apparatus to overcome it. Largely as a result of the work of Trendelenburg[40] and recently of Rochat,[36] there is no doubt any longer that the binocular fusion of colors takes place and that one can get from this method regular color mixing equations resembling those secured monocularly. I have recently[12] described a very simple method of demonstrating binocular fusion of colors which renders it impossible for anyone to doubt its existence and which could be adopted as a routine laboratory experiment.

It must be obvious that if one can produce a white sensation by putting yellow in one eye and blue in the other, there is no use in talking of a special receptor for white. White and yellow are sensations which are produced in the brain out of the impulses that come in from the three receptors in the retina. We may, therefore, conclude that the uniqueness of yellow and white as sensations is no obstacle to adopting Thomas Young's three receptor idea as a basis on which to build a theory for the receptor mechanism of color vision. This does not mean that the ideas which prompted Aubert, Hering, and the others may not be applicable to some other portion of the complicated series of events involved in color vision. That, however, is beside our present point. For the receptor process a three fiber idea is adequate.

III. THE NATURE OF YOUNG'S THREE FIBERS

Having adopted the notion of three receptor elements as a basis for color vision, we are obliged to consider the further specification of the nature of these three receptors. It has frequently been suggested, and with excellent reason, that the three fibers may be considered as three species of cones. In this way there is united the fiber idea of Young with the substance idea of Helmholtz. Each type of cone contains its own photosensitive substance, and is connected with an optic nerve fiber, stimulation of which produces in the brain the corresponding sensation. Let us adopt this notion as a clarifying and a simplifying one, and proceed to the necessary next step in the theoretical treatment of color vision, namely, the quanti-

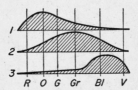

Fig. 1. *Spectral sensibility distribution of Young's three primaries as suggested by Helmholtz (14). The shapes of the curves are entirely diagrammatic.*

tative description of the spectral properties of these three receiving elements.

Efforts to define them have not been lacking. Young originally gave no precise description of his three fibers except to say that their maxima were respectively in the blue, the green, and the red, and that they each were sensitive to the whole spectrum. However, Helmholtz[14] made a drawing of their spectral properties, which, though entirely fanciful, expressed Young's and his notions of them. This drawing is reproduced in Fig. 1. Later, the work of Maxwell,[30] of Koenig and Dieterici,[26] of Abney,[1] and recently of Wright[42] has given us three curves currently known as excitation curves or sensation curves which are supposed to represent the spectral characteristics of the three primaries at the basis of color mixing. These curves are reproduced in Fig. 2. They give the values derived by Weaver from the work of Koenig and Dieterici and of Abney, and have been adopted by the Optical Society[41] as standard primaries. The areas under the three curves are made equal following Koenig's original suggestion that they contribute equally in making white. In terms of them, there is usually constructed the familiar color triangle.

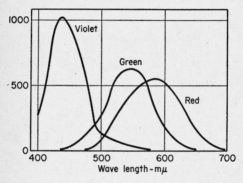

Fig. 2. The excitation curves adopted as standard by the Optical Society of America. The curves are taken from the Report of the Colorimetry Committee (41) and were derived by Weaver by recomputing and averaging the data of Köenig and Dieterici (26) and Abney (1). They correspond essentially to what Koenig and Dieterici called their Elementarempfindungen.

Do these three excitation curves really represent the physiological primaries of Thomas Young? Are they a description of the spectral properties of three fundamental processes concerned with the reception of color? There is a tacit assumption among us that they are, though most of us would never acknowledge this publicly. Certainly Koenig who first derived them accurately felt that they were very nearly the descriptions of the three sensations, though he knew they were not exactly so. Therefore, by making a few linear and homogeneous transformations in their values, he derived from them three curves, which he called the basic sensation curves, or Grundempfindungen, and which he thought might represent these primaries physiologically. These are given in Fig. 3. Koenig never forgot that his three Grundempfindungen were transformed color mixture equations; and when it became necessary later to change their form he did not hesitate to do so.[24] Since Koenig's time the original Grundempfindungen have acquired an air of great respectability; so much so, that the very necessary and important changes, which he made in them after their first formulation, have been consistently ignored and are never referred to in the papers or books of the last thirty years. Koenig always remembered that the

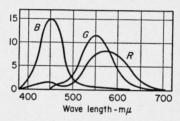

Fig. 3. The Grundempfindungen of Koenig and Dieterici (26). These curves were derived by Koenig and Dieterici by combining in various ways their Elementarempfindungen as given in Fig. 2.

Grundempfindungen, as well as the excitation curves from which they are derived, represent nothing more than the data of color mixture. As such they were brilliant derivations because they showed that the color mixture equations given by the three main kinds of color blind eyes could each be described by means of only two of the three Grundempfindungen which the normal eye yields.

It is quite true that color mixture is one of the most important characteristics—perhaps the most important characteristic of color vision. Nevertheless, it is not the only significant property of color vision. If the excitation curves or the Grundempfindungen are really a description of the spectral characters of the three physiological primaries of Thomas Young, they should furnish an ade-

quate theoretical basis for the other properties of color
vision as well. Unfortunately, the Grundempfindungen
have not served in this capacity. It is usually not recognized that the Grundempfindungen were shown to be
inadequate in this respect almost immediately after their
formulation. This was done by Helmholtz[16] in his treatment of Koenig's data of hue discrimination. Other failures have since become apparent.

I believe that we can learn much from the closer examination of these failures of the excitation curves. Their
inadequacies may perhaps suggest some other specifications for the three physiological primaries of Thomas
Young in terms of which one may describe not only the
data of color mixtures, but of other properties of color
vision as well.

.   .   .

V. THE VISUAL ACUITY OF THE COLOR BLIND

The inadequacy of the excitation curves as a description of the three necessary receptors for a color theory
first became evident to me in trying to understand certain
results which we secured in measuring the visual acuity
of color blind people. Our reasons for undertaking the
measurements were somewhat as follows. It has been
shown that the visual acuity of the eye is proportional
to the number of cones which are functionally present in
a unit area of the retina.[12a] The tri-receptor idea assumes
that there are three kinds of cones. Suppose for the
moment that they occur in the ratio of $1:1:1$. Thomas
Young's explanation of color blindness may then be considered to mean that a red-blind or a green-blind person
lacks one set of cones, the red or the green. Therefore a
dichromat, since he possesses only two-thirds the normal
quota of cones, should have a maximum visual acuity of
only two-thirds normal. Moreover, because of the spectral
distribution of the excitation curves, the visual acuity of a
dichromat should be low in the spectral region which
corresponds to the lost set of cones, and should be normal in the rest.

Our measurements, however, showed no such condition. In the first place, the red-blind and green-blind individuals whom we tested showed in white light a maximal

visual acuity of the same magnitude as normal eyes. This
by itself is not very serious. One may adopt an old idea
of Fick,[10] which was accepted to a certain extent both by
Helmholtz and by Koenig, that a color blind does not
really lose the function of one set of cones. What happens rather is that the sensitive substance in the affected
cones assumes the spectral characteristics of one of the
other kinds of cones. If, for example, in a red-blind person the red-receiving cones should have their substance
take on the spectral properties of the substance in the
green-receiving cones, then such a person would still have
the full quota of cones. But there would be a confusion
of red and green, both of which would appear as yellow.
This is because these lights would stimulate the red-
receiving cones and the green-receiving cones to exactly
the same extent. The impulses going up from these cones
would, however, still register red and green, and since
the impulses would be simultaneous and equal, the brain
would synthesize yellow. Such a person would be color
blind, but since he has the normal number of cones per
unit retinal area, his visual acuity in white light would
be of the same magnitude as that of the normal trichromat. Indeed, the fact that we found dichromats to possess
a normal visual acuity in white light lends considerable
support to Fick's representation of the basis of color-
blindness.

Our next findings, however, were much more disturb-
ing, because while they further supported Fick's idea,
they were not understandable in terms of the notion that
the excitation curves represent the three kinds of cones.
Consideration of Fig. 2 shows that if the red curve, for
example, dropped out, then the visual acuity should be
much reduced in the red end of the spectrum, less so in
the green part, and hardly at all in the blue region. We
found, however, that whereas the visual acuity of a red-
blind is really lower than normal in the red region of the
spectrum, it is distinctly higher than normal in the other
regions. Obviously the red-receiving cones are not lost;
their spectral sensibility is merely changed to correspond
with that of the green-receiving ones. But closer consideration of the data, as well as of the three excitation
curves presents difficulties at once. Doubling the green

curve at the expense of the red curve will result in a loss of the red, an increase in the green, and hardly any change in the blue. Our measurements, however, showed only a slight rise above normal in the green, but a decided increase in the blue corresponding in size to about the loss in the red.

If we try to explain this by supposing the red-receiving substance to take on the properties of the blue-receiving substance we are met with the fact that this does not correspond to the sensations of the color blind as given to us by monocular color-blind individuals. Moreover, we accentuate the paradoxical situation with which we had to deal in the last section with regard to the brightness of the spectrum. Suppose, for example, that the blue, green, and red cones are present anatomically in the retina in the ratio of 1:1:1. Then as we saw before we would need 1 blue to 75 green to 100 red cones to make white. If now in the case of a red-blind person the red cones assume the spectral sensibilities of the blue cones, then white light should call out 1 real blue cone, 75 green cones, and 1 red cone with the blue-receiving properties. And white light would then appear bluish-green to a red blind. We know this is not true from cases of people who are color blind in one eye only. Moreover, in such a case the total number of cones stimulated would be in the ratio of 77 for the color blind compared to 176 for a normal; and the visual acuity of a dichromat in white light should be less than half of normal. This we know not to be true; it is just like normal.

If we take the other supposition that the cones are present anatomically in the ratio of 1 blue to 75 green to 100 red, we are no better off. In the case of our dichromat, what would happen to the 100 red cones whose receiving substance has been changed from red to blue? There would be a large drop in visual acuity in the red as expected; but there would be a relatively enormous increase in the visual acuity in the blue. The matter may be put more effectively if we consider a case with just a trivial loss of red, say 10 per cent. The drop in visual acuity in the red would be insignificant; but the increase in the blue should be fantastically large. However, our experiments show that the decrease in visual acuity in the red is just about compensated by the increase in the blue.

If the excitation curves really described the properties of the physiological primaries which we have here spoken of as cones, then these various findings should be consistent and sensible. As it is they are as confusing as many other phenomena of color vision have been, and point to the fact that the excitation curves are not the correct description of anything else except color mixture data.

. . .

IX. A POSSIBLE HYPOTHESIS

Let us suppose that there are present in the retina three kinds of cones; blue-receiving cones, green-receiving cones, and red-receiving cones. Let us further suppose that in the fovea they are present in approximately equal numbers. The spectral properties of these cones will be described presently. At first it is well to understand what we mean by the first assumption. We suppose that a given cone, possessing a photosensitive substance whose absorption is normally greater in the blue, or in the green, or in the red part of the spectrum, is joined to a nerve fiber which is so connected with the brain that whenever the photosensitive substance in the cone is changed by light and starts an impulse in the nerve, that nerve will register respectively blue or green or red in the brain. It means moreover that no matter what method may be used to start this impulse, no matter what the wave length of the light may be, indeed no matter what the photosensitive substance in the cone may be, an impulse travelling up a "blue" nerve will register blue in the brain, a "red" nerve red, and a "green" nerve green.

The spectral characteristics of these three types of cones—practically their absorption spectra—are given in the curves in Fig. 7 and in detail in Table 1. It is apparent that these three curves are radically different from both the excitation curves of Fig. 2 and the Grundempfindungen of Koenig in Fig. 3. Since it is their quantitative properties which will be used to describe in detail various phenomena of color vision it is important to tell something about the origin and formulation of these new primaries. Otherwise the matter will appear too arbitrary to be useful for further work and thought.

TABLE 1

Primaries V, G, and R tentatively proposed as a description of the three receptors postulated by Young as a basis for color vision. V, G, and R add up directly to give Ives' luminosity curve L.

λ	V	G	R	L
410	2.5	1.4	0.1	4
420	5.9	3.7	0.5	10
430	9.9	6.1	2.0	18
440	15.3	9.3	4.4	29
450	21.5	12.8	7.7	42
460	28.1	17.6	12.4	58
470	38.7	29.5	21.8	90
480	53.5	48.8	35.7	138
490	75.0	78.5	58.6	212
500	113.6	124.6	97.8	336
510	144.6	175.4	160.1	480
520	196.7	229.9	211.4	638
530	248.9	284.3	262.9	796
540	289.2	325.1	303.7	918
550	313.9	348.4	329.8	992
560	321.6	346.2	331.2	999
570	310.2	325.6	317.2	953
580	278.1	299.4	301.5	879
590	234.0	256.3	267.7	758
600	190.7	212.7	229.6	633
610	146.9	161.4	181.7	490
620	103.0	119.4	139.7	362
630	69.4	81.7	99.0	250
640	44.4	52.4	67.2	164
650	26.5	30.3	43.2	100
660	15.8	16.6	27.6	60
670	9.9	10.0	19.1	39
680	4.8	5.0	12.2	22

Essentially they were specially designed to account for precisely those properties of color vision which we have found to be impossible of description in terms of the excitation curves. Naturally, therefore, they had to include those properties of the excitation curves which are useful in the description of color mixture, and to a certain extent of color blindness. Like the excitation curves, our primary curves have certain specific crossing points. The red and the green curves cross at about 575 $m\mu$ to account for yellow; the violet and the green curves cross at about 490 $m\mu$; the violet and the red curves cross at about 500 $m\mu$. These take care of certain complementary color equations, as well as of the neutral points of the three types of color blind individuals. Like the excitation curves they are equal in area; but unlike them, they add up very simply to give the visibility curve of the spectrum of white light.

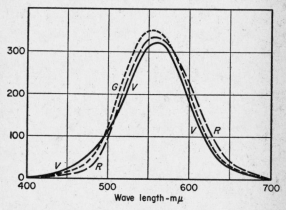

Fig. 7. *Spectral distribution of the primaries, V, G, and R, here tentatively proposed as a basis for a quantitative treatment of color vision.*

A study of the different properties of color vision shows that we may arrange them in a sort of hierarchy of magnitudes, each ascending magnitude being more restrictive than the other. If we accept the crossing points as stated above and demand that the areas of the curves be equal we can draw an infinite series of curves which will satisfy this demand. The excitation curves are just one of this infinite variety. The primary curves in Fig. 7 are another. If we demand in addition that the three equal primary curves shall add up to give a normal visibility curve we at once limit the positions of these curves, though there are still a large number of curves which will satisfy this added requirement. If we further restrict the shapes of

these curves with the demand that they yield the data of
color mixture as adequately as the excitation curves do,
it is apparent that the possible types of curves, though
still large, are more reduced than before. From now on
any additional demands that may be made of the primaries have a surprisingly restricting effect. For example,
when the requirements of visual acuity are added the
curves become so restricted that one may draw them free-
hand to a first degree of approximation. Once these
curves have been secured in this approximate way quantitative investigations may be begun on them to see how
the various properties of color vision are derived from
them, and how systematic changes in them yield different
quantitative relations. I do not wish to minimize the
labor involved in such a procedure; it is pretty large.
Nevertheless it is worth recording that once the relations
between the different sets of data of color vision were
mastered and understood, the first approximate primary
curves were not difficult to draw, and were not very dissimilar from those given in Fig. 7.

It is interesting to point out some peculiarities of these
relations. For example, color mixture equations are not
very different for different people. This is apparent from
the extensive data of the past, but more particularly from
the recent investigations of Wright shown in Fig. 4. On
the other hand hue discrimination is a very delicate and
distinctly individual affair. Steindler's data show this well,
as do the data of Laurens and Hamilton. It is important
to remember such things when one tries to invent a set
of primaries to account for the data of color vision, because unfortunately, one has to use data from different
individuals for the different functions. Individual differences will thus not be very apparent in color mixture
equations but will show up strikingly in hue discrimination. Therefore in making the primaries it is well to
satisfy the latter requirements first.

Before proceeding to show how the three primaries
drawn in Fig. 7 describe the various data of color vision,
I wish to call attention to one minor point. You will
notice that although I have previously spoken of blue
cones, the corresponding curve which I have presented
in Fig. 7 is marked violet rather than blue. This is be-

cause violet seems to act as a unit in equations of color mixing and in several other things as well. For the moment, however, I wish to leave this paradox aside. I shall take it up later and show how it may be resolved.

. . .

XIII. COLOR BLINDNESS

Reference has already been made to color blindness, and before concluding this paper it is necessary to develop this aspect to a slight extent. It may as well be confessed that color-blindness is the subject that I have thought least about, and therefore it is in the least satisfactory condition. Nevertheless it is necessary to discuss the matter in order to point out the weak points as well as the strong ones.

It has already been shown that we must extend the original notion of Thomas Young that color blindness means the simple loss or inactivity of one of the three kinds of receptors. This was apparent to Fick, as well as to Koenig and to others. What we know requires us to adopt the notion that in color blindness the spectral characteristics of one of the receptors is changed so that it becomes identical with one of the others. For example let us suppose that the photosensitive substance in the green-receiving cone becomes changed so that its absorption spectrum (and probably its chemical constitution) becomes identical with that in the red-receiving cones. Under such circumstances the changed green-receiving cone and the red-receiving cone will be equally stimulated by any light. However, the rest of the mechanism remains undisturbed; that is, the "green" fiber will still cause a green sensation in the brain as before. Therefore there will be no way for such an eye to discriminate hues in the spectrum between about 550 $m\mu$ and 700 $m\mu$, all this region appearing predominantly yellow. That this is true we know first from the reports of those people who are color blind in one eye and normal in the other; and second from the studies on the hue discrimination of color blinds by Steindler and by Laurens and Hamilton. Moreover, since the heights of the V and the R curves are identical at about 490 $m\mu$, the curve of the changed "green" substance, since it is like the "red" will also cross the V curve at the same spot. But, since the sensations produced will still be violet, green, and red in equal amounts the result will be a white sensation, or the neutral point in the spectrum of the green-blind.

The same situation arises if the substance in the "red" cones take on the absorption spectrum and the photochemical properties of the substance in the "green" cones. The sensations produced by the spectrum will be predominantly blue from about 400 to 500 $m\mu$, and predominantly yellow from 500 to 700 $m\mu$, with a white or neutral point at about 500 $m\mu$. These neutral points will be the regions of greatest hue discrimination because of the great changes that the V curve on the one hand and both the G and R curves on the other show toward each other. An exactly analogous state of affairs would result if the substance in the blue-receiving cones were to become converted into either the "red" substance or the "green" substance. There would be a white spot, or neutral point at about 575 which would be the region of greatest hue change. The information about the hue discrimination and neutral points of color blind individuals is entirely consistent with these deductions.

I am convinced, however, that color blindness cannot be completely described in such comparatively simple terms. What further ideas and limitations must be added it is not possible to say at this moment. But it is necessary to indicate where the weak spot is, so that further work and thought may be directed to it. It concerns the luminosity distribution of the spectrum for color blinds. We know from the excellent measurements of Brodhun[4] and others that the luminosity of the spectrum for the green blind, or deuteranope, does not differ significantly from the normal. Although adequate measurements are not available for the blue-blind or tritanope, it is probable that this type also has a practically normal distribution of brightness in the spectrum. Both these facts are readily understandable in terms of the V, G, and R curves. The curves are so similar that an exchange of one for another does not materially affect the luminosity distribution in the spectrum. Certainly it would be difficult to be sure of any such difference what with the large individual variations in the luminosity function and the relative uncertainty of heterochromic photometry.

The case of the red-blind or protanope is strikingly different. It has been known for years,[23] and the fact has been repeatedly verified,[9] that the luminosity distribution in the spectrum is very different for the protanope as compared with the normal or the deuteranope. The maximum is shifted toward the short-wave end of the spectrum. The luminosity is sharply depressed in the long-wave end, and it is correspondingly increased in the short-wave region. This is known relatively from the luminosity measurements themselves, and is corroborated by the enhanced visual acuity in the same region in proportion to its reduction in the long-wave end. The simple transformation of the R curve into the G curve, though it is in the right direction, is not adequate in magnitude. The resulting change in brightness is only about a fourth of what is necessary to describe the data obtained by Koenig,[23] by Exner[9] and by others.

I have been unable to suggest any additional changes which, when combined with the transformation of the "red" substance into the "green," would account for the singular character of the luminosity function of the red-blind, and at the same time remain consistent with all the other things that are known about color blindness. For example, the obvious suggestion that the V, G and R curves be separated more than they are at present does not help matters. Their present separation is practically the maximum possible provided their areas are kept about equal. My judgment is that the V, G and R curves are already separated more than necessary. This is because I at first thought that their separation could be made to account for the red-blind luminosity. However, some other derivation will be required to adjust this difficulty, and I hope that one of the effects of the presentation of the ideas in this paper will be such a formulation by someone else.

XIV. BLUE AND VIOLET

It has been apparent that the spectral distribution curve of one of the three cone primaries has been labelled

V. This is because violet seems to act as a unitary thing in color mixture, and in hue discrimination, and I wished to stick as close to the data as possible. Nevertheless, one cannot ignore the fact that blue, like yellow or red is a unique sensation, whereas violet is a color blend obviously compounded of blue and red. It is for this reason that I spoke in Section ix of a blue-receiving cone rather than a violet-receiving cone.

Koenig got out of this dilemma in the first construction of his Grundempfindungen[26] by calling the curve B and by assuming that the red sensation curve has a secondary maximum in the short wave part of the spectrum and crosses the green sensation curve in the same region. After his investigations with tritanopes or blue-blinds, Koenig[24] abandoned this idea because this type of color blind showed only one neutral point, at 575 $m\mu$, and failed to show a neutral point at the supposed crossing of the red and green curves in the violet end of the spectrum. He then chose his Grundempfindungen to be violet, green, and red, even though most people have ignored his later work and have quoted only his former.

The argument from the blue-blind neutral point is perfectly valid and it is for this reason that I have also chosen V as the designation of the spectral distribution of one of the primaries. Curiously enough, the most recent study of a blue-blind person, unfortunately reported only in a very sketchy form,[6] established a neutral point in the violet end of the spectrum. If this turns out to be the real condition, then Koenig's first choice of a blue Grundempfindung and a secondary crossing of the red and green curves will have to be reconsidered.

So far as the V, G, and R curves are concerned the situation is the same. At present the G and R curves cross but once. If the secondary neutral point of the tritanope becomes established, then it is a simple matter to make the G and R curves cross at about 420 $m\mu$ and to designate the third curve by B and not by V. No quantitative relations of any size are changed by such a procedure because of the relatively trivial alterations required in the R and G curves to accomplish this. In the meantime, however, one may keep the V, G, and R curves as they are. But that leaves us the dilemma of a V curve and a "blue" cone.

It is not a very difficult dilemma to resolve, and I give one possible solution here more for its interest than for my belief in it. Let us assume that all normal people are very slightly red blind. Suppose that the photosensitive substance in a small fraction, say 10 percent, of the red-receiving cones takes on the spectral characters of the substance in the blue-receiving cones. Then any light which normally affects the blue cones more than the red or green cones will also affect these red cones with the blue substance in them. This will be particularly the case at the short wave end of the spectrum. But the sensation which results from the stimulation of the originally-red-but-now-blue cones is still red. The result of this will be a constant association of a certain fraction of red sensation with the pure blue sensation, which gives the appearance of violet. Thus though violet is a blend it will behave like a unit in color mixture and in other quantitative aspects of color mixture.

This idea is perhaps capable of an experimental test. If the number of red, green, and blue cones are about equal in the fovea, and some of the red cones have taken on the properties of the blue, then the area under the resulting violet curve should be larger than that under either the green or the red; and the area under the red curve should be less than that under the green. Just how to ascertain this, I do not at present know. I, for one, hope that Dieter's discovery[6] of a secondary neutral point for blue-blinds is confirmed; that would facilitate and simplify the whole situation because then one could have a B curve, and a crossing of the R and G curves.

XV. FINAL CONSIDERATIONS

Reduced to its bleakest terms, what I have presented here is a series of relationships between well-known data. These data are often inadequate because they have been secured by various observers whose color systems may be sufficiently different to obscure their relations. Therefore, I hope that no one will consider these ideas and computations as a final statement. Indeed, the situation is precisely the reverse. Experiments are exciting in proportion to the ideas which determine their existence. Many measurements and many experiments must be made before we can understand color vision. My present paper is thus largely a program. It represents the general ideas which are orienting us in our laboratory in an attack on the theoretical structure of color vision.

Thomas Young one hundred and thirty years ago suggested the original idea for a theory of the mechanism of color vision. We have seen that this original idea is adequate as a foundation on which to build a theory. What I have tried to show is that when this idea is made precise and quantitative, and when there is added to it the suggestions of other workers, like Helmholtz, Koenig, and Fick, it is possible to account accurately and adequately for many previously obscure and unrelated but very important phenomena of color vision. Thomas Young's contribution to color vision is thus a beautiful leaf in the wreath of his scientific achievement. I hope that this leaf will continue to be green and vigorous for many years to come.

BIBLIOGRAPHY

[1] Abney, W. de W. Researches in color vision. London, 1913.

[2] Adrian, E. D. *Die Untersuchung der Sinnesorgane mit Hilfe elektrophysiologischer Methoden.* Ergebn. der Physiol., 26, p. 501; 1928.

[3] Aubert, A. Physiologie der Netzhaut. Breslau, 1865.

[4] Brodhun, E. Beiträge zur Farbenlehre. Dissertation. Berlin, 1887.

[5] Brückner, A. *Zur Frage der Eichung von Farbensystemen.* Z. f. Sinnesphysiol., 1927, 58, p. 322; 1927.

[6] Dieter, W. *Über die subjektiven Farbenempfindungen bei angeborenen Störungen des Farbensinnes.* Z. f. Sinnesphysiol., 58, p. 73; 1927.

[7] Erlanger, J., and Gasser, H. S. *Analysis of the action potential in nerve.* The Harvey Lectures, Series 22, p. 90; 1926-1927.

[8] Exner, F. *Über die Grundempfindungen in Young-*

Helmholtz' schen Farbensystem. Sitzungsber. Akad. Wiss., Wien, *111*, IIa, p. 857; 1902.

9 ———. *Helligkeitsbestimmungen im protanopen Farbensystem*. Sitzungsber. Akad. Wiss., Wien, *130*, Abt. IIa, p. 355; 1921.

10 Fick, A. Die Lehre von der Lichtempfindung. In L. Hermann, Handbuch der Physiologie, iii., Part 1, p. 139. Leipzig, 1879.

11 Forsbes, A. The mechanism of reaction. In C. Murchison, The Foundations of Experimental Pychology, p. 128, Woreester, 1929.

12 Hcht, S. *On the binocular fusion of colors and its relation to theories of color vision*. Proc. Nat. Aecad. Sci., *14*, p. 237; 1928.

12a Hecht, S. *The relation between visual acuity and illumination*. J. Gen Physiol., *11*, p. 255; 1928.

13 Hiecke, R. *Neue Folgerungen aus den Farbenempfindungskurven von A. Koeng und C. Dtt erici*. Z. f. Sinnesphysiol., 58, p. 111; 1927.

14 eHelmholtz, H. Handbuch der physiologischen optik. Hamburg and Leipzig, 1st edition, 1866.

15 ———. Popular lectures on scientific subjects. Translated by E. Atkinson, London, 1881.

16 ———. *Versuch das psychophysische Gesetz auf die Farbenunterschiede trichromatischer Augen anzuwenden*. Z. f. Sinnesphysiol., 3, p. 517; 1891.

17 Hering, E. Grundzüge der Lehre vom Lichtsinn. Berlin, 1920.

18 Ives, H. E. *The transformation of color mixture equations from one system to another. II. Graphical aids*. J. Franklin Inst., p. 23; 1923.

19 Jones, L. A. *The fundamental scale for pure hue and retinal sensibility to hue differences*. J.O.S.A., 1, p. 63; 1917.

20 Judd, D. B. *Chromatic visibility coefficients by the method of least squares*. J.O.S.A. & R.S.I., *10*, No. 6, p. 635; 1925.

21 ———. *Sensibility to color change determined from the visual response functions; extension to complete and partial dichromasy*. J.O.S.A. & R.S.I., 1928, *16*, p. 115; 1928.

[22] Koenig, A. Ueber die neuere Entwickelung von Thomas Young's Farbentheorie. In A. Koenig, Gesammelte Abhandlungen zur Physiologischen Optik, Leipzig, p. 88, 1903.

[23] ————. Ueber den Helligkeitswerth der Spectralfarben bei verschiederer absoluter Intensität. In A. Koenig, Gesammelte Abhandlungen zur Physiologischen Optik, Leipzig, p. 144, 1903.

[24] ————. Ueber "Blaublindheit." Sitzungsber. Akad. Wissensch., Berlin, p. 718; 1897.

[25] Koenig, A., and Dieterici, C. *Ueber die Empfindlichkeit des normalen Auges für Wellenlängenunterschiede des Lichtes.* Wiedem. Ann. Physik u. Chem., 20, p. 579; 1884.

[26] ————. *Die Grundempfindungen in normalen und anomalen Farbensystemen und ihre Intensitätsverteilung im Spektrum.* Z. Psychol. u. Physiol. Sinnesorgane, 4, p. 241; 1892.

[27] v. Kries, J. Die Gesichtsempfindungen. In Nagel's Handbuch der Physiologie des Menschen, Braunschweig, 3, p. 109; 1905.

[28] Ladd-Franklin, C. Colour and colour theories. New York, 1929.

[29] Laurens, H., and Hamilton, W. F. *The sensibility of the eye to differences in wave length.* Am. J. Physiol., 65, p. 547; 1923.

[30] Maxwell, J. C. *On the theory of compound colors and the relations of colors of the spectrum.* Scientific Papers, Cambridge, 1, p. 410; 1890.

[31] Mayer, A. M. *The history of Young's discovery of his theory of colors.* Am. J. Sci. and Arts, Series, 3, 9, p. 251; 1875.

[32] Müller, J. Handbuch der Physiologie des Menschen. Coblenz, 1840.

[33] Newton, I. Opticks. Book 3, Queries, 13, 14, and 16. London, 1704.

[34] Peddie, W. Color Vision. London, 1922.

[34a] Priest, I. G. *A precision method for producing artificial daylight.* Phys. Rev., 9, p. 502; 1918.

[35] Priest, I. G., and Brickwedde, F. G. *The minimum perceptible colorimetric purity as a function of dominant*

wave length with sunlight as neutral standard. J.O.S.A. & R.S.I., *13*, p. 306; 1926.

[36] Rochat, G. F. *Étude de mélange binoculaire de rouge et de vert.* Arch. neérl. de Physiol., *10*, p. 448; 1925.

[37] Schrödinger, E. *Über das Verhältnis der Vierfarben- zur Dreifarbentheorie.* Sitzungsber. Akad. Wiss., Wien, *134*, Abt. IIa, p. 471; 1925.

[38] Sinden, R. H. *Studies based on spectral complementaries.* J.O.S.A. & R.S.I., 7, p. 1123; 1923.

[39] Steindler, O. *Die Farbenempfindlichkeit des normalen und farbenblinden Auges.* Sitzungsber d. k. Akad. der Wiss., Wien, *115*, Abt IIa, p. 39; 1906.

[40] Trendelenburg, W. *Weitere Versuche über binokulare Mischung von Spektralfarben.* Arch. ges. Physiol., *201*, p. 235; 1923.

[41] Troland, L. T. *Report of the colorimetry committee of the Optical Society of America.* J.O.S.A., 6, p. 527; 1922.

[42] Wright, W. D. *A re-determination of the trichromatic coefficients of the spectral colours.* Trans. Opt. Soc., *30*, No. 4, p. 141; 1928-29.

[43] Young, T. On the theory of light and colors. In Lectures in Natural Philosophy, London 2, p. 613. 1807.

LABORATORY OF BIOPHYSICS,
  COLUMBIA UNIVERSITY,
    NEW YORK CITY.

10

The Theory of Colour Vision

ROBERT A. HOUSTON

111. Let us state the conditions which a theory of colour vision must satisfy:

(1) The sensation of light is mathematically a function of three variables. All sensations can be produced by combining three stimuli.

(2) Although the sensation is a function of three variables, it cannot be the sum of three separate sensations of brightness, as the preceding reasoning shows. It seems reasonable to assume one sensation of brightness and two sensations of colour, or one sensation of colour and one sensation of saturation.

(3) The colours red and green and yellow and blue are connected in pairs. This is required by the great body of tradition connected with Hering's theory.

(4) Yellow according to the psychologists is a fundamental sensation. We cannot see the red and green in it. Here we are on less certain ground, because for me spectrum violet has always been a fundamental sensation, and the psychologists appear to regard it as composite. But the case of yellow is, I think, beyond doubt.

(5) Anatomically there is no evidence for three photochemical substances or three nerve systems. But there are two nuclear layers and two reticular layers in the retina.

This selection is from the book by Robert A. Houston, *Vision and Colour Vision*, New York: Longman's, Green, and Co., 1932, pp. 226-229; 231-232. Reprinted by permission.

It is in this last condition that I think the solution lies. According to the usual view the nervous impulse originates in the layer of the rods and cones, passes through the outer nuclear layer, crosses a synapse in the outer reticular layer, passes through the inner nuclear layer, and then crosses a synapse in the inner reticular layer. There are thus two synapses in the visual path. But as far as I can make out from inspection of the drawings and conversation with workers in this field, it is impossible to trace the single fibres with certainty. An alternative interpretation is thus equally probable, namely, that there are two different kinds of visual path, those with a synapse in the outer reticular layer and those with a synapse in the inner reticular layer. The distance between the two layers is so small that a separate neurone seems hardly necessary to carry the impulse from the one to the other. I would suggest, with all the ignorance of a physicist, that the cells are arranged in two layers, so that the cones can pack closer.

Let us assume that there are two different kinds of path. To satisfy the requirements of Hering's theory we have to make a further assumption, namely, that after the synapse each path transmits only two kinds of impulse. Or in other words, there are red-green fibres which transmit either red or green, and blue-yellow fibres which transmit either blue or yellow. If R and P denote respectively the number of red-green fibres in the red and green states and B and Y the number of blue-yellow fibres in the blue and yellow states, since the number of fibres in each class is the same,

$$R + P = B + Y$$

As the four variables are connected by this relation, only three of them are independent. Thus the laws of colour mixing are satisfied.

112. It will conduce to clear ideas if we trace the process from the start. Light of a certain frequency falls upon a photochemical substance, and electrons are ejected according to the equation of the quantum theory

$$h\nu = \tfrac{1}{2}mv^2$$

The velocity of the electron depends on the frequency of

the light and the number ejected on the intensity of the light.[1] These electrons set up pulses in the cones. R. S. Lillie[2] has described a nerve model which imitates very closely the propagation of the pulses. If an iron wire is dipped into a strong solution of nitric acid, its surface becomes "passive," i.e. becomes covered by a sheath of oxide which protects it from the further action of the acid. If the wire is then immersed in a weaker solution of the acid and its surface touched with a zinc rod, the sheath is destroyed at the point of contact, and a pulse characterized by effervescence travels rapidly along the wire. The shell reforms behind the pulse, and after a short interval of time the wire is in a condition to transmit another pulse. Now the time of recovery will depend to some extent on the velocity of the electrons, i.e. on the discharging potential. We think, therefore, of a train of pulses of variable frequency approaching the synapse from the cone, the frequency varying according to the colour of the incident light.

Beyond the synapse there are only two possible frequencies, e.g. in the case of the red-green fibres the fibre must be either in the red or the green state. Perhaps the analogy of an organ pipe may be helpful. If we blow it gently, it sounds the fundamental; but if we blow harder, it gives the first harmonic.

Thus the light process and the colour process are quite separate. One takes place in the layer of the rods and cones and the other in the reticular layers. If the light has a certain intensity, the same fibres are stimulated, no matter what is the colour. But the proportions existing in the different states depend on the colour. This picture may be speculative and fanciful, but I can think of no other in harmony with the facts. I use the symbol P to denote the number of fibres in the green state, because I regard the sensation caused by this state to be peacock-blue rather than green.

116. Explanation of Colour Blindness.—Colour blindness is due to an irregularity in the working of the

[1] The number and velocity of the electrons are exactly analogous to quantity and potential in the electrical stimulation of a nerve-muscle preparation.
[2] Cf. p. 43.

napse. In the normal eye all the red-green nerves do not
ange from the one state to the other at exactly the
me wavelength, but the transition points are spread
·er a region. In the case of the colour different, those
ho have a good but abnormal perception of colour, this
gion is displaced, usually towards the green. In the
·se of the colour weak, those who can match colours
·rrectly but with an immense effort, this region is in the
·rrect position but much wider than usual. Colour dif-
·rence and colour weakness usually occur together. The
napse is susceptible to the action of drugs: hence
·bacco colour blindness.

The deuteranopes are the colour blind who have a visi-
lity curve which is high in the red and the protanopes
·ose who have a visibility curve low in the red, but
·ese differences in the visibility curve are due to normal
·riation, and are not connected with the difficulty in
·scriminating colour. Thus the classification into deuter-
·opes and protanopes is an artificial one. This was the
·ew of Hering, who considered that there was only one
·nd of red-green blindness, although he was not very
·ecided about the matter. I feel, however, quite certain on
·is point. I admit, of course, that on the whole the litera-
·re of the subject, particularly that due to physicists,
·ows a division of the cases into two classes, but I think
·servers have been subconsciously influenced by the
·oung-Helmholtz scheme into throwing away their transi-
·onal cases. In the Glasgow surveys we worked through
· very large normal "population"; any one who showed
·normality was detained for investigation and cases who
·esented themselves from outside this population were
·refully kept apart. Only in this way can certainty be
·tained; an investigator must not allow himself to be
·tracted by cases that are "interesting" or "good ob-
·rvers." Fig. 88 * shows that in a population of 500
·rmal variation will allow sensibility to the red end of
·e spectrum to vary over a range of from one to twenty
·mes.

* (Not included in this excerpt)—Eds.

11

A Physiological Theory of Colour Perception

RAGNAR GRANIT

*Neurophysiological Laboratory, Karolinska Institutet
Stockholm*

It is nowadays possible to record the discharge of the
retinal elements directly by leading off to electrodes from
more or less isolated fibres of the optic nerve. The electrical impulses following upon illumination are the
physiological means of communication between the retina
and the higher centres. They are amplified and led to an
oscillograph for photographic recording and at the same
time listened to in a loud-speaker. This is the technique
for which the well-known work of Prof. E. D. Adrian
and his collaborators originally laid a solid basis. For
isolation of the fibres in the optic nerve a method of
micro-dissection around the blind spot has been developed by Hartline[1] and a micro-electrode technique
for picking up from the fibres inside the eye by Granit
and Svaetichin.[2] The latter method is a great deal
simpler and faster than the former, and for this reason
it is the natural instrument for a rapid survey of the
colour properties of a large number of single or grouped
units in the response of the eye to illumination with
spectral light of known energy content. Mammalian eyes
can be studied with the micro-electrode as easily as eyes
of the cold-blooded animals, to which the technique of
micro-dissection is limited if it is to be used for analytical
purposes. The animal is anaesthetized, cornea and lens re-

This selection originally appeared in *Nature*, 151, 1943, pp.
11-14. Reprinted by permission.

moved, and the micro-electrode inserted with the aid of a micro-manipulator under suitable optical magnification.

Successful isolation, in mammals particularly easy to accomplish, leads to a discharge of spikes of impulses (Fig. 1). In different elements a response follows onset of illumination or both onset and cessation of illumination, as first noted by Hartline[1] with the frog's eye. In the latter and in some other eyes, there are also elements which merely respond to cessation of illumination. But these different types of responses are of less interest in

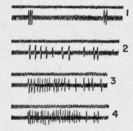

Fig. 1. Impulses picked up by a micro-electrode placed on the nerve fibres inside the retina. Above each oscillogram is the time record (50 per sec.) and light signal. 1, "on-off"-element from photopic cat's retina responding to light of wave-length 0.660. Somewhat above threshold. 2-4, "On"-element from scotopic retina of guinea pig responding to "white" light: 2, at strength 0.006 m.c.; 3, at 0.018 m.c.; and 4, at 0.061 m.c. Note increasing frequency and shortening latent period, as stimulus intensity increases.

this connexion because of the absence of any definite correlation between type of discharge and type of colour sensitivity, to judge by the work so far carried out.

In order to analyse the colour sensitivity of such discharges, we proceed to measure the amount of energy necessary for eliciting a threshold response in the different wave-lengths of the spectrum. If the element under the electrode has low sensitivity for light of a given wave-length, much energy is needed to elicit a discharge; if it has high sensitivity, little energy is required. Thus the inverse value of the energy necessary for a threshold response in each wave-length is the ordinate (per cent of the maximum) plotted in the curves of Figs. 2 and 3, illustrating the spectral properties of the retinal receptors. I shall briefly direct attention to some results of general interest from work published during 1940-42 (*Acta Physiologica Scandinavica*; preliminary review, *J. Amer. Opt. Soc.*, 31, 570 (1941)). Since then the number of animals studied has been extended and principles have merged which in my opinion suggest a relatively simple

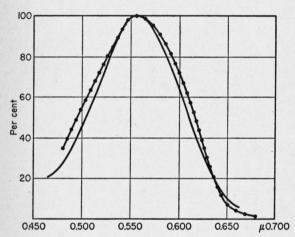

Fig. 2. *Distribution of sensitivity of "dominator" element in the retina of frog (uninterrupted line) and snake (line interrupted by dots).*

interpretation of some of the fundamental facts of colour vision, particularly of the differentiation of our sensations into the two categories of brightness (or luminosity) and colour. The principles discovered may also be of practical importance.

Analytically, the simpler structure is the dark-adapted eye with its rods fully charged with visual purple. We are familiar with the absorption curve of this substance. It was first accurately determined, with in every respect satisfactory and up-to-date technique, by the late R. J. Lythgoe,[3] of University College, London. Our electrophysiological analysis of eyes of different animals in dark-adaptation has shown that a plot of the inverse value of the energy necessary for a threshold response reproduces the absorption curve for visual purple with perfect fidelity, provided that the curves are corrected for presentation in terms of quantum intensity, a necessity first pointed out by Dartnall and Goodeve[4] in *Nature*. The

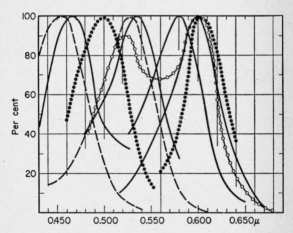

Fig. 3. Distribution of sensitivity of "modulator" elements from eyes of rat (dots), guinea pig (broken line), frog (line in full) and snake (line interrupted by circles). Note that all curves are in percentage of the maximum and that a number of ordinates on either side of 0.560 μ are drawn down to indicate "dominator" values. All spectra of equal quantum intensity in both Fig. 2 and Fig. 3.

maximum of this absorption curve is around 0.500μ. Visual purple also determines the luminosity curve of the dark-adapted human eye to the region of 0.56μ (Purkinje shift) and the new curve obtained determines the distribution of brightness in a spectrum strong enough to elicit sensations of colour (photopic spectrum). As is well known, the retina is then supposed to utilize cones as receptor elements.

In light-adapted eyes of animals the simple spectral

sensitivity curves recorded with the micro-electrode technique are of two types: (i) broad absorption bands, here called *dominators*; and (ii) narrow bands, here called *modulators*. The most interesting fact about the photopic dominator, apart from the width of the curve, is the localization of its maximum to the region around 0.560μ, as shown in Fig. 2 for frog and snake (Tropidonotus), the latter a pure cone eye which need not be light-adapted to give this curve. The same dominator has been found in the eye of the cat. The dominator is lacking in the eyes of guinea pigs and rats. The form and spectral locus of the dominator is practically identical with the average curve obtained from massed receptors in the light-adapted eyes of the same species. In this sense the dominator may be called the carrier of the Purkinje shift. This and its good correspondence with respect to form and locus with the luminosity curve of the light-adapted human eye necessitate the conclusion that the dominator is responsible for the sensation of brightness, which thus is our dominant impression, coming, as it does, from the dominant receptor, dominant also in the sense that it is the most frequent one.

How then is colour vision possible? Modulation of the dominant impression of brightness to colour would seem to be the task of the much rarer modulators which occupy very narrow bands of sensitivity in three preferential regions around 0.580-0.600μ, 0.520-0.540μ and 0.450-0.470μ. These are shown in Fig. 3. In addition, there is also in some eyes (rat, guinea pig) a narrow band in the region of 0.500μ, which is the spectral locus of the maximum of the absorption curve for visual purple. The rat has 1 per cent cones, the guinea pig still less, if any. It is an interesting fact that in these eyes, which lack dominator and Purkinje shift, light-adaptation does not completely remove the absorption curve for visual purple but changes it to a very much narrower curve of modulator type, still placed in the same region. Light-adapted rods in this case serve as cones.

The most regularly recurring modulator in the different species studied has been the 'red' one with maximum at 0.600μ. It has even been found in the eye of the rat, which lacks the dominator, but not in guinea pigs. In the cone eye of the snake the 'red' modulator was generally, though not always, connected to a 'green' hump at 0.520μ, which sometimes was more, sometimes less, developed. Its narrowness (see Fig. 3) suggested a 'green' modulator which, however, was never obtained in the isolated state in this animal. But in guinea pigs and frogs 'green' modulators with maxima around 0.530μ were seen. The 'blue' modulator was first found in the eye of the frog, then in the guinea pig. In both retinae it is quite common in the shape of a hump on other curves, but it is difficult to isolate. The frog, of all the animals studied, has the most complete set of modulators (cf. Fig. 3). As rods and cones may converge towards a common retinal ganglion cell (Polyak[5]), and as many other factors antagonize isolation, it is clear that all attempts to interpret complex curves as well as to understand the nature of the sensory message as a whole must begin by emphasizing the positive character of the evidence for the existence of curves as simple as the modulators. Complex curves with several humps are, of course, common.

The experiments with the cone-eye of the snake suggested that the dominator itself is composed of modulators joined together in such a fashion—either photochemically or by connexions in the retinal synapses—as to operate as a *functional unit*. However, this assumption though probable, is not essential to the theory based on the experiments. But it would explain why stimulation of all modulators together also causes an impression of white, and not of all colours confused. The modulators would in this case merely add to the effect of the dominator. Alternatively, the modulators could be coupled in antagonistic pairs which simultaneously neutralized each other at the retinal or some higher level. As a matter of fact, in eyes where both 'red' and 'green' modulators are present, they are very difficult to isolate from each other.

But let us now see what kind of theory of colour vision would be a direct consequence of the experimental subdivision of the receptors into a great number of almost identical dominators and a smaller number of narrow modulators varying somewhat in shape, locus, sensitivity and number within three preferential spectral regions. No further assumptions will be introduced beyond the original one, that the dominator stands for the dominant impression of brightness, and is modulated by the modulators so as to give the higher centres a cue for their integration of 'colour.'

(1) The greater the distance in the spectrum from the centre of the dominator the darker the colour. Colours towards the ends of the visible spectrum must be dark by comparison with those near the top of the dominator. This we know to be true.

(2) W. D. Wright[6] has shown that selective adaptation of the human eye to any colour causes chiefly a large general reduction of brightness and an insignificant selective effect on the fatiguing colour. This also is a direct consequence of a dominator for the perception of brightness. Classical theories would seem to require not only a much larger selective effect on the fatiguing colour but also a considerable shift of the luminosity curve.

(3) As it is improbable that all receptors would be exactly the same threshold, a diminution of intensity should, on classical theories, lead to perception of coloured spots. Instead, we know that it leads to the spectrum becoming colourless, with the brightness distribution of the dominator, as required by the presence of this most common receptor.

(4) Similarly, a reduction of area of the visual object, which is known to lead to disappearance of its colour with maintained brightness distribution, must do so because the 'small' stimulus merely has a chance of hitting upon the common dominators.

(5) Colour-blindness need not, but *can* be possible without parallel change of the photopic luminosity curve. A colour-blindness of this type would be the common form of red-green blindness known as deuteranopia, to be interpreted as absence of the 'red' and 'green' modulators, with the remaining dominator alone giving the normal luminosity curve. Without a separate structure for the perception of brightness as distinct from colour, no theory can ever hope to explain colour-blindness unaccompanied by considerable 'luminosity blindness' to light from the 'blind' region of the spectrum.

Many of the animals studied represent different types of colour-blindness if considered from the point of view of the complete colour sense of man. The guinea pig probably comes very near the totally colour-blind, the cat near the deuteranope. The cat has the typical dominator but no definite 'red' modulator. The guinea pig, however, has a number of different modulators in the short wavelengths and hence may be able to discriminate colours in this region. But it lacks dominator and Purkinje shift. The totally colour-blind human has a photopic luminosity curve practically identical with the luminosity distribution of the normal dark-adapted eye dominated by visual purple. The guinea pig has the same scotopic *and* photopic sensitivity curve, slightly distorted by a hump in the blue in the photopic state.

With the three preferential regions for the modulators, it is clear that this theory can do what the trichromatic theory does and also that it demonstrates the essential correctness of Thomas Young's great generalization, although it is necessary to assume a greater or lesser number of somewhat different modulators within these regions. The main crux of the trichromatic theory and, indeed, of any classical theory, is the lack of precision in the concepts accounting for the perception of white as a separate entity which, nevertheless, somehow is intimately connected with the perception of colour. The trichromatic theory regards white as due to the summed effects of, chiefly, the 'red' and the 'green' sensitivity curves. This forces the theory to accept the consequence that removal of 'red' and/or 'green' should cause removal of the perception of luminosity in the same region of the spectrum. Hence there can be no colour-blindness without profound changes in the form and locus of the luminosity curve. It is an admission of failure to have to explain so important a phenomenon as deuteranopia by pushing it aside to be taken care of by the 'higher centres.'

Many of the phenomena to which the trichromatic theory has directed attention need not be discussed for the reason that my theory does not necessarily exclude the explanations already available. Thus, for example, the fineness of colour discrimination in different regions of the spectrum may be explained in the classical way, or else by the assumption that the number of slightly different modulators is particularly great in the regions where the maxima of colour discrimination are placed.

In its present form the theory gives no explanation of contrast colour, though certain alternatives seem reasonable in view of the fact that different elements are so often coupled together and that the retina contains a large number of coupling synapses. If a certain percentage of the 'red' and 'green' modulators are coupled together in such a manner that both are forced to discharge when either is stimulated, the natural result to expect from the asymmetry caused by fatiguing either of them is that the other one should predominate in the neighboring region as well as in the off-effect. The experiments themselves have not yet dealt with situations calculated to bring forth contrast phenomena.

It is impossible in this brief review to deal with the available evidence concerning the nature of the colour-sensitive substances. The hypothesis I prefer is that visual purple—which may be called the dominator of the scotopic eye—is the mother substance for the photopic dominator and the modulators. Its molecule consists of a protein nucleus serving as carrier for about ten chromophoric groups (see Broda, Goodeve and Lythgoe[7]). The different sensitive substances may be due to changes in the linkage between carrier and chromophorea.

REFERENCES

1. Hartline, *Amer. J. Physiol.*, 121, 400 (1938).
2. Granit and Svaetichin, *Upsala Lakaref. Forh.* N.F., 45, 161 (1939).
3. Lythgoe, *J. Physiol.*, 89, 331 (1937).
4. Dartnall and Goodeve, *Nature*, 139, 409 (1937).
5. Polak, *Arch. Ophthalm.*, 15, 477 (1936).
6. Wright, *Proc. Roy. Soc.*, B., 115, 49 (1934).
7. Broda, Goodeve and Lythgoe, *J. Physiol.*, 98, 397 (1940).

12

General Statement of the Theory

EDWARD N. WILLMER

In the human eye, rods and cones are quite certainly the significant receptor elements. There is no indication on structural grounds of the presence of more than one type of cone. On phylogenetic, embryological and functional grounds, the rods and the cones show themselves to be elements which have diverged along quite different lines, in a manner comparable with the divergence displayed, for example, by the sympathetic and parasympathetic divisions of the autonomic nervous system. They form two distinct, and to some extent mutually antagonistic, forms of receptor cells, each with its own spectral sensitivity.

Dark-adaptation is probably to be regarded as a specialisation of the receptor cell which depends upon visual purple, namely, the rod. It is therefore not improbable that the rods function not only in dim light but also under conditions when colour vision is possible. It is suggested that there may be found to exist in the eye certain rods (here called non-adapting or day-rods) which, though they depend for their spectral sensitivity upon visual purple, have either never acquired, or have lost, the power of dark-adaptation. There is evidence that the spectral sensitivity of a dark-adapting rod under photopic conditions may not be the same as its sensitivity under scotopic conditions. The breakdown products of the accumulated visual purple may be instrumental in deter-

The following article is excerpted from Willmer's book *Retinal Structure and Colour Vision* (Cambridge University Press, 1946, pp. 212-214, excerpted) in which the various parts of his theory are argued. Although this is not a full statement of his theory, it gives good coverage of his ideas. Reprinted by permission.

mining this change. Dark-adapting rods and day-rods, therefore, may not have the same spectral sensitivities under daylight conditions.

It is thus possible that among the actual receptor cells of the eye there are three clearly defined types. These would be (1) the cone, (2) the dark-adapting rod, and (3) the non-adapting or day-rod. Each would have its own spectral sensitivity, thereby fulfilling the essential condition for complete colour vision, namely, the presence of at least three independent types of receptor, with distinct spectral sensitivities. Of these suggested receptors the day-rod is somewhat hypothetical, and, of course, it is not yet proved that the dark-adapting rod does actually function in daylight. Nevertheless, among other evidence for the existence of the day-rod, it may be mentioned that in the frog there is a definite class of rods which do not demonstrably possess visual purple.

The primary receptor cells relay on to bipolar cells, and of these there are three fairly well-defined groups. These are (1) the cone or midget bipolar, (2) the flat bipolar, with its variant the brush bipolar, and (3) the mop or rod bipolar. Of these the midget bipolars occur throughout all regions of the retina and make individual connections with the cones, and with the cones only. The flat bipolars make connections with both rods and cones. They are nevertheless present over the entire retina, including the central fovea, which has usually been regarded as rod-free. The mop bipolars connect primarily with rods, though they may make contact with the outer surface of cone pedicles. They are not present among the bipolar cells connecting with the *fovea centralis.*

The central fovea behaves as a diplodic system, that is to say, it seems to have only two independent receptor pathways. It is tritanopic. Histological evidence points to the existence of two pathways, namely, *via* the midget bipolar and *via* the flat bipolar respectively. It is therefore suggested that the receptors in the *fovea centralis* are (1) the cones relaying by way of the midget bipolars and (2) the non-adapting or day-rods and cones relaying together by way of the flat bipolars. The foveal centre can see and appreciate all the spectral colours from violet to red, though certain confusions will occur if the intensities

of the colours are varied: higher threshold intensities of
blue and violet are required than elsewhere in the retina.
Colour charts could therefore be constructed either in
terms of the sensitivities of these two foveal receptors, or
in terms of the responses given by the receptors. Such
charts could be effectively used to describe the phenomena of colour mixing, saturation, hue discrimination,
effects of changing the intensity of the light and of adding white light to spectral colours as well as various other
phenomena, in so far as such things affect the fovea
only, or, if the whole retina is used, are confined to the
colour range of reds, yellows and greens in which the
intervention by the third receptor is minimal. The charts,
which are two-dimensional, of course break down to some
extent when applied to the whole eye, because a third
factor is operative in the blue region of the spectrum.
The general properties of the charts, however, indicate
that the two receptors whose activities they describe are
probably the dominant elements in colour vision and the
third factor or receptor, acts as a modifier, to stamp the
particular sensations with unique properties rather than
to determine new sensations.

The third receptor, not present in the fovea, is diag-
nosed as the ordinary dark-adapting rod relaying by way
of the mop bipolar, and there are several reasons for believing that it may be inhibited by the cones; its activities
as a distinct type of receptor are almost confined to the
blue end of the spectrum, though it may possibly become
important again in the extreme red when the light intensity is such as to allow the rods to increase their sensitivity by means of the accumulation of visual purple.

It thus seems theoretically possible to account for the
phenomena of colour vision on the basis of physiologically and histologically acceptable data, postulating only
one element, instead of two, for which there is no direct
evidence; even for this element there are good *a priori*
grounds for believing that it may exist. The fundamental
sensations can on this hypothesis be correlated with the
activities of known structures in the eye, and the three
necessary pathways are provided to satisfy the demands
of the century old Trichromatic Theory.

13

Recent Advances in Colour Vision

H. HARTRIDGE, F.R.S.

SECTION 1
INTRODUCTION

Many theories of colour vision have been suggested from time to time. Most of them have received little support, but two have been exceptions in this respect, namely, Young's three-colour theory and Hering's four-colour theory. The former is in apparent conformity with colour mixture and with colour deficiency data, while the latter is superficially in agreement with other important aspects of human colour vision. The polychromatic theory to be dealt with in this address is the outcome of an attempt to combine together the good features of both these older theories.

According to Young's theory human colour vision is provided by a tricolour unit. On the other hand, according to Hering's theory it is provided by two units: a yellow-blue unit and a red-bluegreen-red unit. The polychromatic theory proposed by the author adopts the tricolour unit as its principal agent and the yellow-blue and red-bluegreen-red units as its subsidiary agents. Thus human colour vision is nearly trichromatic but not quite, because in addition to the tricolour unit there are also present the two additional units just mentioned.

Here then is an outline of the polychromatic theory.

Polychromatic theories have been advanced by Wundt, by Edridge-Green, and in a modified form by Shaxby.

This article originally appeared in *Advancement of Science*, Vol. 5, 1949-59, pp. 243-245; 251-253. Reprinted by permission.

Granit's modulators also form, in some animals, what amount to a polychromatic series. The polychromatic theory advanced by the author differs from all these in important respects, and it is not proposed to deal further with them here, but instead to describe briefly the circumstances which lead to the development of this particular theory.

Until a few years ago experimental work appeared to support unequivocally the three-colour theory of Thomas Young. When the author first observed the change of yellow to pale grey or white, and of blue to dark grey or black, which play so essential a part in the antichromatic responses, he endeavoured, apparently with success, to account for them on this classic theory. But further facts then came to light incompatible with that theory. These facts were: (1) the change in the shape of the luminosity curve with reduction of light intensity, and the development of a notch (Sloan, 1928); (2) the corresponding change in the shape of the luminosity curve with reduction of visual angle (Willmer and Wright, 1945); (3) the finding by the author (1947) of more fixation points in the fovea than three; (4) the finding by the author of more specific colours than three, as the result of applying microstimulation to the retina in the presence of suitable conditioning stimuli. These results, incompatible with the three-colour theory, led to a re-examination of the whole subject of colour perception.

The outcome of that survey convinced the author that, under average conditions of lighting, adaptation and field size, the three-colour theory is a useful approximation so far as foveal vision is concerned. It is the truth but not the whole truth because it is not in accord with a large mass of evidence, much of which has been obtained recently, partly by using improvements on older methods, such as the mixture of spectral colours by means of the Wright spectroscope, and partly by the development of entirely new methods—for example, the Stiles and Crawford technique. But much older work was also found at variance with the three-colour theory. When all this evidence has been taken into account it would not be unfair to sum up by stating that there is hardly a single phase of human colour vision which does not support a polychromatic theory more strongly than it does one based only on three colours.

SECTION 2

THE POLYCHROMATIC THEORY

The polychromatic theory postulates the existence of two subsidiary visual units in addition to the tricolour unit of Young's theory. One of these, the Y-B unit, has receptors with response curves having crests in the yellow and in the blue parts of the spectrum. The other unit—the R-BG-R unit, also comprises two types of receptors and these have response curves with crests in the red and in the bluegreen part of the spectrum, but the former have in addition secondary curves in the extreme violet part of the spectrum. This fact is indicated by the duplication of R in the title of the unit.

When the fovea is being used in normal colour vision all three units are in action. When a more peripheral part of the retina is in use the Y-B unit alone provides colour vision. The fovea at very high light intensities also employs this unit alone, whereas at low intensities or small visual angles the R-BG-R unit functions alone. With white stimuli, all the constituent receptors of the functioning units receive adequate stimulation. When, on the other hand, the objects under examination are coloured, then the receptors which are stimulated are those which have response curves in the corresponding part or parts of the spectrum, and which belong to functioning units. The following example may make this clearer: suppose the ray incident on the retina to be red of 0.65μ, then the stimulated receptors are the long wavelength receptor of the tricolour unit, the red receptor of the R-BG-R unit and the yellow receptor of the Y-B unit. If the ray which falls on the fovea is of medium light intensity all three units will be potentially in action and the sensation aroused by their combined actions will be a somewhat orange-red.

At very high intensities, however, as stated above, the only active unit is the Y-B one, and in consequence the sensation aroused by the stimulus of wavelength 0.65μ

will be yellow. At low intensities the only active unit is the R-BG-R one, and the sensation aroused will consequently be a purplish crimson, since this is the hue produced by the activity of the red receptor of this unit which, as stated above, has response curves both in the red and in the violet parts of the spectrum. These theoretical conclusions agree with experiment.

These three units together comprise seven different types of receptor and these have eight response curves, the spectral positions of which are indicated in Table 1.

TABLE 1

Visual Unit	Position of Receptor in the Spectrum	Probable Wavelength of Crest of Response Curve
Tricolour	Orange	0.610
Tricolour	Green	0.545
Tricolour	Indigo	0.450
Y-B	Yellow	0.575
Y-B	Blue	0.473
R-BG-R	Red and Violet	0.670 / 0.360
R-BG-R	Bluegreen	0.495

The wavelengths shown in the last column are approximate only.

When white light falls on the retina it stimulates all receptors of active units. Thus at the fovea under medium light intensities all seven receptors will be active, at high intensities the yellow and the blue receptors only, at low intensities the red and the bluegreen receptors only. At the dichromatic zone of the periphery of the retina the yellow and the blue receptors are those which are stimulated, because the Y-B unit is the only one which is potentially active. This accounts for the large sizes of the yellow or blue fields in comparison with those of red and green. It is clear therefore that according to the present polychromatic theory all seven types of receptor are in use only at medium light intensities at the fovea and the parafovea. At other intensities and in the periphery of the retina a simpler receptor arrangement is in use. As the visual angle is reduced, first the Y-B unit becomes inactive, then the tricolour unit, finally leaving the R-BG-R unit alone in action. The author has produced evidence that these changes are not limited to the foveal centre but take place in all parts of the retina where all the three units are normally in action.

SECTION 3
HUE DISCRIMINATION

It will be remembered that there are two classes of subject who are able to pass successfully the ordinary tests for colour blindness; these are the normal trichromats and the anomalous trichromats. The latter are subdivided into two classes according as they require more red or more green, than the normal sighted, in order that a red-green mixture shall match a given yellow. Those who require more red and are therefore somewhat red-blind are called protanomalous, since they approximate to the completely red-blind or protanopic. Those who require more green and are therefore somewhat green-blind are called deuteranomalous, since they approximate to the deuteranopic subject.

There are two varieties of protanomalous trichromat: a primitive type and a more advanced type. The hue discrimination curve of the former consists of two U-shaped parts, having troughs at about 0.49μ and 0.59μ. To account for this curve three types of receptor are required, namely: in the long, medium and short wave region of the spectrum. The hue discrimination curve of the better type of protanomalous subject, such as Wright's observer A, shows improvement in the green part of the spectrum. To account for this improvement an additional receptor is required, probably in the blue-green part of the spectrum. Investigation shows that an alteration of position, or a change of width, of the response curve of one of the three receptors mentioned above, does not bring about the improvement shown on comparing the curves.

The colour vision of the normal subject as found by Pitt and Wright (1934) shows improvement at about 0.44μ over that possessed by observer A, and there is a second region of improvement near the orange part of the spectrum. To account for these improvements two additional types of receptors are required, in the blue and the yellow. Finally, some normal-sighted observers, such as Steindler (1906), Jones (1917), Laurens and Hamilton (1923), appear to have better hue discrimination still, particularly in the red part of the spectrum. This calls for an additional type of receptor.

Calculations of the hue discrimination curve of normal-sighted subjects have been made by Helmholtz (1896), Judd (1932), Stiles (1946), and others, on the basis of the three-colour theory. These calculated curves are far from being identical in shape with the experimental curves obtained with normal-sighted, protanomalous (including Wright's observer A) and deuteranomalous observers, as should be the case, because according to the three-colour theory all these three classes are 'trichromats.' Thus the three-colour theory fails to give a satisfactory account of the hue discrimination of these subjects. The polychromatic theory, on the other hand, postulates three types of receptor for the more primitive protanomalous subject, four types for the more advanced type, probably five types for the deuteranomalous and seven types for subjects with normal colour vision.

SECTION 12

SOME OTHER RECEPTOR ARRANGEMENTS

When alternative hypotheses to the polychromatic theory were examined by the author particular attention was paid (a) to modifications of the three-colour theory; (b) to three-channel hypotheses.

One modification of the three-colour theory has already been referred to in this address, namely, linking between the red and the green receptors at the fovea at high light intensities and at the periphery of the retina, and linking between the green and the blue receptors at the fovea at low light intensities and at small visual angles. Of all the modifications of the classical three-colour theory this seemed to the author to be the most promising. It fails, however, mainly for three reasons: (a) it gives no expla-

nation of the changes in shape of the luminosity curve;
(b) it gives no adequate account of the differences of
colour vision between the true trichromats, that is of
subjects with normal sight, on the one hand, and between
the protanomalous and the deuteranomalous on the other;
(c) it does not comprise the necessary number of different types of receptor to comply with the requirements of
the phases of vision referred to in sections 3, 4, 5, 8, 9
and 11 of this communication; in consequence there is
no alternative but to abandon this attractive hypothesis.

Of the three-channel hypotheses one of the best known
is that proposed by Granit himself soon after his discovery in the mammalian retina of modulator response
curves. His suggestion was that the nerve pathways from
the orange and the yellow modulators might converge
on to a single channel, that the three green modulators
might do the same, and similarly for the two blue ones.
Thus there would be polychromatism in the retina but
trichromatism in some part or parts of the nervous channels between the receptors and the brain, and possibly
in the brain itself. Le Gros Clark (1941), as the result
of a histological survey of the external geniculate body of
the monkey, has proposed that this structure forms a
part of this triple channel. Now there can be little doubt
that this hypothesis is in certain respects an improvement
on the preceding one; thus the polychromatism of the
retina offers an explanation of the retinal direction effects
which depend on local conditions. It also accounts for
the many different fixation points. Important facts which
it cannot deal with are spectral mixture, hue discrimination and the essential differences between the normal-
sighted subject and the anomalous trichromat, all of
whom must use the same three channels if this hypothesis is correct. But apart from these general criticisms
there are some special ones, because Le Gros Clark has
claimed that the periphery of the retina is dichromatic,
with yellow and blue as primary colours. But this is only
true at moderate intensities of illumination and ceases
to be so if the light intensity be increased. He has also
claimed that the fovea is dichromatic, with red and blue-
green as primary colours. But in this case also the dichromasy is conditioned by light intensity and disappears if

this be increased. Lastly, the external geniculate body, if Le Gros Clark's description be correct, contains no provision for a channel connecting the rod receptors with the brain. If this does not pass through the external geniculate body, what course does it pursue? These are but a few of the difficulties which beset this three-channel theory.

Of four-colour theories the only one which need claim attention here is that originally proposed by Hering (1874), because it is representative of the others. The four most likely receptor types have response curves with crests in the red, the yellow, the bluegreen and the blue, but the red receptor also has a subsidiary response in the violet part of the spectrum; in consequence the best types of receptors comprise five response curves. Since the red and the bluegreen receptors are complementary, and since the former also acts in the violet, they form a unit which may be identified as the R-BG-R unit of the polychromatic theory. In the same way the yellow and blue receptors of Hering's theory, since they are complementary, may be identified as the Y-B unit of the polychromatic theory. Thus Hering's theory in a modern form may be regarded as similar to the polychromatic theory, from which the tricolour unit has been omitted. What then would be the disadvantages of doing this? For normal foveal vision both units would be in operation. On reducing light intensity or visual angle the Y-B unit would drop out leaving the R-BG-R unit alone in action. At high light intensities the Y-B unit would be the only effective one. The same unit would operate when there is dichromasy of the retinal periphery. Since these units comprise complementary pairs of receptors the constancy of white under all these conditions is satisfactorily accounted for. The varieties of colour blindness are not so readily explained. Protanopia might be due to the Y-B unit, and deuteranopia to linkage of the yellow and the red receptors to form a single receptor mechanism together with the corresponding linkage of the bluegreen and the blue receptors to form the second receptor mechanism. Protanomaly might be caused by linkage of the red and the yellow receptors, the green ones and the blue ones acting separately. Deuteranomaly might be caused by linkage of the green and the blue, the red and the yellow receptors acting separately and so on. Where the four-colour theory fails most obviously is when it attempts to fit in with hue discrimination data.

An examination of other theories leads to the final conclusion that only the polychromatic theory is in agreement with all the known facts, and that this must extend not only along the nervous channels which connect the receptors to the brain but must also apply to the brain itself.

SUMMARY

Until a few years ago it was possible to account for nearly all the aspects of human colour perception on the basis of the three-colour theory, but such is no longer the case. This is largely due to improvements in the older methods of investigation and to the invention of new ones. Among the latter may be mentioned the micro-electrode technique of Granit and the retinal direction effect of Stiles and Crawford. Modern requirements are met by a polychromatic theory, comprising seven types of receptor, but there is no necessity for these to have such narrow spectral response curves as those exhibited by Granit's modulators. Modifications of the three-colour and four-colour theories have been examined to see to what extent they can be made to fit in with experimental results. Particular notice has been taken of the possibility that there is polychromatism of the retinal receptors but trichromatism of the nerve paths which connect these to the brain, or even to the brain itself.

The conclusion arrived at is that there must be polychromatism throughout the entire visual mechanism for colour perception if a complete account is to be given of all the known facts.

REFERENCES

ALLEN F., 1908: Trans Roy. Soc. of Canada, 2, 195.
BURCH, G. J., 1898: Phil. Trans. Roy. Soc. London, B, 191, 1.

———, 1900: *F. Physiol.* 25, 17P.

Chapane, A., 1944: *Journ. Exper. Psychol.* 34, 1. Feb.

Crawford, B. H. and Stiles, W. S., 1933: *Proc. Roy. Sec. B*, 112, 428.

Edridge-Green, F. W. and Marshall, D., 1909: *Trans. Ophthal. Soc.* 29, 211.

Fick, A. E., 1888: *Arch f.d. ges. Physiol.*, Bonn, Bd. xliii. S. 445 (Sch. Vol. II, p. 1056).

Franklin, 1894: *Sitzungsb. d. k. Akad. d. Wissensch.*, Berlin, S. 589 (Sch. Vol. II, p. 1088).

Granit, R., 1947: *Sensory Mechanisms of the Retina.* Geoffrey Cumberlege, Oxford University Press.

Hamilton, W. F. and Laurens, H., 1923: *Amer. J. Physiol.* 65, 547.

Hartridge, H. 1947: *Phil. Trans. B*, 232, 592.

———, 1948: *Proc. Physiol. Soc.*, 10 Jan., J. Physiol., Vol. 107.

Helmholtz, H. v., 1896: *Handb. d. Physiol. Optik.*, 2nd Edit., 448.

Hering, E., 1874: *S. B. Akad. Wiss.*, Wien, 69, 179.

Holmgren, A., 1880: *Centralbl. f. d. med.* Wissensch., Berlin, S. 898 and 913 (Sch. Vol. II, p. 1094).

Horner, R. G. and Purslow, E. T., 1947: *Nature*, 160, 23.

Ivanoff, A., 1947: *Revue d'Optique*, 26, 145.

Jones, L. A., 1917: *J. Opt. Soc. of Amer.* 1, 63.

Judd, D. B., 1932: *J. Opt. Soc. of Amer.* 22, 72.

Kries, J. v., 1896: *Ztschr. f. Psychol. u. Physiol. d. Sinnesorg.*, Hamburg u. Leipzig, Bd. ix. S. 81; and Bd. xii. S. 1 (Sch. Vol. II, p. 1102).

———, 1897: *Zeit. B. Psych. u. Physiol. der Sinnesorg.*, 15, 247.

Laurens, H. and Hamilton, W. F., 1923: *Amer. J. Physiol.* 65, 547.

Le Gros Clark, W. E., 1941: *J. Anatomy*, 75, Part 4, July.

MacAdam, D. L., 1947: Communication to Colour Vision Conference at Cambridge.

Marshall, D. and Edridge-Green, F. W., 1909: *Trans. Ophthal. Soc.* 29, 211.

Pitt, F. H. G., 1944: *Proc. Roy. Soc. B*, 132, 101.

Purdy, D. McL., 1931: *Amer. J. Psychol.* 43, 541.

Purslow, E. T. and Horner, R. G., 1947: *Nature*, 160, 23.

Shaxby, J. H., 1947: *Nature*, 160, 24.

Sloan, L. L., 1928: *Psych. Mon.* 38, No. 1.

Steindler, O., 1906: *Sitz. d. Wiener Akad.* iia, 115, 39.

Stiles, W. S., 1937: *Proc. Roy. Soc. B*, No. 830, 123, 90-118.

————, 1946: *Proc. Phys. Soc.* 58, 41.

Stiles, W. S. and Crawford, B. H., 1933: *Proc. Roy. Soc. B*, 112, 428.

Thomson, L. C., 1946: *Nature*, 157, 805.

Wilbrand, 1896: *Die Erholungsausdehnung des Gesichtsfeldes*, S. 42 (Sch. Vol. II, p. 1088).

Willmer, E. N. and Wright, W. D., 1945: *Nature*, 156, 119.

Wright, W. D., 1936: *J. Physiol*, 87, 23.

————, 1942: *The Refractionist*, 31, 53.

————, 1946: *Researches on Normal and Defective Colour Vision*. Henry Kimpton, London.

Wright, W. D. and Willmer, E. N., 1945: *Nature*, 156, 119.

14

An Opponent-Process Theory of Color Vision

LEO M. HURVICH AND DOROTHEA JAMESON
New York University

The two major theoretical accounts of color vision are those classified as the Young-Helmholtz and the Hering types of theories. For many years the former has been judged by most workers in the field to provide the simplest explanation of the way in which light stimuli give rise to color sensations. The advantages that appear to favor the Young-Helmholtz three-component hypothesis are two: it is parsimonious, and its postulates are easily quantifiable and hence subject to precise experimental test. In its parsimonious and easily quantifiable form, the theory is simple: in addition to the rods which subserve twilight vision, the eye contains three kinds of cone photoreceptors; each type of cone contains a differently selective photochemical substance; each is associated with its own specific nerve fiber; and each cone-photochemical-nerve fiber system is correlated with one of the three specific "fundamental" color sensations, namely, red, green, and blue (or violet). All sensations are considered as compounded of varying amounts of these three excitatory systems, with white arising from equal and simultaneous excitation of all three, and yellow from equal red and green excitations.

The Young-Helmholtz three-cone, three-nerve, three-sensation theory derives directly from the basic fact of color mixture, namely, that all visible hues can be matched by the mixture, in proper proportions, of only

This article originally appeared in the *Psychological Review*, 1957, Vol. 64, pp. 384-390; 397-404. Reprinted by permission.

three physical light stimuli. Based squarely on this fact, the theory is readily quantified in terms of the three measurable variables of color mixture experiments. But the three measured variables, it must be emphasized, are the three physical light stimuli used in the color mixture experiments; they are not the postulated three "fundamental" color sensations, for with each different stimulus triad used for color matching a different and equally valid triad of color mixture functions is obtained. Consequently, throughout some hundred years since the original formulation of the idea, a continued series of attempts has been made to find the proper transformation of the three measured color-mixture curves that will bridge the gap and yield the unique spectral distribution curves of the desired physiological correlates of the three postulated "fundamental" color sensations. An infinity of such transformations is available for trial, and almost every serious adherent of the theory has proposed at least one new set of "fundamental sensation curves" (48, pp. 368-372). The search, however, continues, because serious defects have been found in every proposal made thus far. When the explanatory or predictive power of the theory in any given quantified form is tested it cannot handle more than a limited number of facts satisfactorily (11, p. 805).

Moreover, some facts of color experience seem unassimilable into the framework of the simple Young-Helmholtz theory with its three independent, fundamental, process-sensation systems. How can this system of three independent processes be made to account, for example, for the apparent linkages that seem to occur between specific pairs of colors as either the stimulus conditions or the conditions of the human observer are varied? Why should the red and green hues in the spectrum predominate at low stimulus levels, and the yellow and blue hue components increase concomitantly as the spectrum is increased in luminance (43)? Why, as stimulus size is greatly decreased, should discrimination between yellow and blue hues become progressively worse than that between red and green (4, 10)? Why should the hues drop out in pairs in instances of congenital color defect, or when the visual system is impaired by disease (29, 31)?

On the other hand, since the sensation of white is granted no special physiological process in this parsimonious theory, but occurs as the fusion product of three equally large fundamental hue sensations, how account for the large degree of independence of white and chromatic qualities when the adaptation of the visual system is varied (37, 41)?

As more and more *ad hoc* hypotheses are added to the original Young-Helmholtz formulation in order to answer these and other problems forced by the increasing accumulation of experimental data, we naturally find the formulation becoming less and less precise and quantifiable, and obviously less parsimonious. We also find, however, that exactly those phenomena that require modification and extension of the simple "three-color theory" remind us more and more of its chief theoretical rival, the Hering theory of three paired, opponent color processes.

In view of this situation, it seems highly desirable that we take a close second look at Hering's alternative approach to an understanding of color phenomena. The vast accumulation of psychophysical data for which any adequate theoretical proposal must account requires that the basic postulates of the theory, as outlined qualitatively by Hering (13, 14), be restated in quantitative terms for such a critical scrutiny to be most meaningful. This paper will review our attempt to provide such a quantitative restatement, and will summarize briefly some of the critical comparisons between the theoretical deductions and relevant psychophysical data. (Detailed quantitative accounts are given in 21, 22, 23, 25, 26, 27.)

BASIC SCHEMA FOR THE HERING THEORY

The Three Variables

The Hering theory is like the Young-Helmholtz theory in that it, too, postulates three independent variables as the basis for color vision, but the Hering variables are three pairs of visual processes directly associated with three pairs of unique sensory qualities. The two members of each pair are opponent, both in terms of the

opposite nature of the assumed physiological processes
and in terms of the mutually exclusive sensory qualities.
These paired and opponent visual qualities are yellow-
blue, red-green, and white-black.

The basic schema for the opponent-colors mechanism
is shown diagrammatically in Fig. 1. The three paired
opponent response systems are labeled *y-b*, *r-g*, and *w-bk*.
The convention of positive and negative signs is used to
indicate that each neural system is capable of two modes
of response that are physiologically opponent in nature,
and that the paired sensory qualities correlated with these
opposed modes of response are also mutually opponent

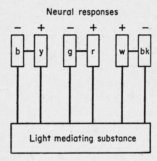

Neural responses

Fig. 1. Basic schema for Hering opponent-colors mechanism.

or exclusive. That is, we may experience red-blues or
green-blues but never yellow-blues, and we see yellow-
greens or blue-greens, but never red-greens, and so on. In
the absence of any external visual stimulus, the state of
the visual system is assumed to be a condition of active
equilibrium, and this equilibrium condition is associated
with the neutral, homeogenous "gray" sensation perceived after a long stay in complete darkness. This sensation is quite different from the black experience of the
white-black opponent pair. Blackness arises neither by
direct light stimulation nor in the simple absence of light,
but rather by way of either simultaneous or successive
contrast during, or following, light stimulation of some
part of the retina.

Properties of Paired Systems

The three pairs of visual response processes are independent of each other; that is, they have different response thresholds, they follow different laws of increase with increase in strength of stimulation, and probably have different time constants. The achromatic system is the most sensitive; that is, the amount of photochemical absorption necessary to excite the achromatic white response is less than the amount of photochemical activity required to stimulate either the *y-b* or *r-g* chromatic pairs. This characteristic accounts for the existence of the so-called achromatic interval, i.e., the fact that spectral lines appear achromatic at the absolute threshold for visibility (42, p. 167). Similarly, the red-green system has a lower threshold than the yellow-blue one. The failure of the yellow-blue system to respond at near-threshold levels that are sufficient to activate the red-green system exhibits itself in the facts of so-called "small field dichromasy," in which the eye behaves, with respect to stimuli that are very small in area as well as of low intensity, in a manner similar to the congenital tritanope, i.e., a specific type of "color blind" individual for whom yellow and blue discriminations are impossible and the only hues seen are reds and greens (4, 49).

With increase in level of stimulation the different paired systems also show differences in rate of response increase, such that the achromatic response increase is probably the most rapid of the three, with the result that at very high intensities all spectral stimuli show a strong whitening, or desaturation, relative to their appearance at some intermediate luminance level (42, p. 168). Of the two chromatic pairs, the yellow-blue system, although exhibiting a higher threshold, shows a more rapid rate of increase in response with increase in luminance than does the red-green system. Thus, the mixed hues of the spectrum—the violets, blue-greens, yellow-greens, and the oranges—all vary systematically with increase in spectral luminance, and all show a tendency to be more blue or yellow, respectively, at high luminances, and more red or green at the lower luminance levels (the Bezold-Brücke hue shift phenomenon).

The opponent systems show a tendency toward restoring the balanced equilibrium condition associated with the neutral "gray" sensation. Thus excitation, say, of the r process in the r-g system results in a decrease with time in r responsiveness, and in an increase in the responsiveness of the opponent g process. If we think of the r process as perhaps associated with the building up of an electrical potential in the neural system, and of the g process as associated with the collapse of the potential during impulse firing, then it is easy to see that as the neural potential is increased to higher values there will be a tendency to resist further build up, and also an increased disposition of the tissue toward impulse firing in order to restore the potential to its normal equilibrium value. Although we are not at all ready to ascribe a specific neural correlate of this sort to the postulated opponent processes at this time, the neurophysiological parallels are useful for conceptualizing the opponent-process notion as a real biological phenomenon.

To return to our example, if the responsiveness of the opponent g process tends to increase as r excitation is continued, then when the r stimulus is removed we can expect g activity to be released, strongly at first, then more slowly, and ultimately fading out as equilibrium is again approached. The sensory correlate of this reversal of opponent activities with removal of stimulation is, of course, the familiar phenomenon of the complementary after-image. If the stimulus (of constant magnitude) is not removed but continues to act for a considerable length of time, then the r process, whose responsiveness is being continuously decreased, will eventually cease to respond further, and a new equilibrium state will be reached. The disappearance of a sensory response with continued constant stimulation can be observed either by the *Ganzfeld* technique, in which the whole retina is uniformly illuminated by diffuse light (18), or by the "painted image" technique, in which optical means are used to fix a well defined image on the retina in such a way that its retinal position remains constant and independent of eye movements (39). By either method the eventual result of continued steady stimulation is a disappearance of the visual experience: the light seems to have gone out in the *Ganzfeld* situation, or, in the fixed-image situation, the perceived object simply fades out of view.

Not only are the visual responses modified by changes in time in the excitabilities of the opponent processes, but they are also importantly affected by spatial inter-action among the various elements of the visual field. Within certain limits there is evidence of summation of similar kinds of activity in adjacent elements, as in threshold responses for small stimulus areas (5, pp. 846-852). But perhaps more important for the over-all functioning of the visual system are the antagonistic interactions, such that *r* activity in one area induces *g* activity in adjacent areas, and similarly for the yellow-blue and white-black paired response systems. These opponent spatial induction effects are evident in all the familiar color and brightness contrast phenomena (35, pp. 138-142). They are probably also primarily responsible for the great visual-image clarity that characterizes vision in spite of the fact that the optical system of the eye is obviously imperfect, and that consequently the light image formed on the retinal surface lacks sharply defined boundaries (17, pp. 151-159). The spatial interaction causing intensification of opponent qualities at adjacent surfaces would seem an ideal crispening device to sharpen up the initially blurred retinal image.

Photochemical Postulates

In addition to the various temporal and spatial induction effects, which are assumed to be based in the neural visual-response tissue, visual adaptation probably also involves changes in the photochemical activities that initiate the neural responses, since a certain amount of photochemical bleaching is expected to occur with continued exposure of the photosensitive materials to a retinal light stimulus. In order for the three paired opponent-response systems to be selectively stimulated, there must, of course, be more than one substance available for photochemical mediation between the incident light and the neural excitation. Whatever the specific nature of the photosensitive materials, they must form a link in the system of three independent variables, and hence we have postulated three independent photosensitive materials, which we may call α, β and γ.

Our schematic model now takes the form shown in Fig. 2A or 2B. The three independent photosensitive

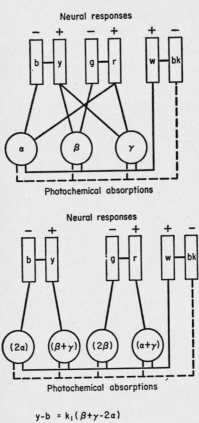

$$y-b = k_1(\beta+\gamma-2\alpha)$$
$$r-g = k_2(\alpha+\gamma-2\beta)$$
$$w-bk = k_3(\alpha+\gamma+\beta)-k_4(\alpha+\beta+\gamma)$$

Fig. 2. Schematic diagram showing relations between photosensitive materials α, β, and γ and neural opponent response processes y-b, r-g, and w-bk.

materials may be contained in discrete retinal units with complex interconnections to the neural response systems, as shown in Fig. 2A, or two or more of these materials may be combined in receptor units having simpler connections to the neural response systems, as diagrammed in Fig. 2B. There is no way of differentiating these models in terms of visual behavior; and however the three photochemicals may be segregated or combined in the retina, and whatever the number of different photoreceptor units, there remain only three independent photosensitive materials, and the theory remains a three-variable, opponent-colors schema.

QUANTIFICATION OF OPPONENTS THEORY

Since our aim is to present this schema in quantitative terms, one of the first questions that has to be asked is this: Is it possible to obtain by psychophysical experiment direct measurements of the spectral distributions of the three basic response variables of the Hering theory?

Measures of Achromatic and Chromatic Responses

It can fairly be assumed that the achromatic, white response is closely connected with the distribution of the brightness quality throughout the visible spectrum, and Fig. 3 therefore shows two functions (which we have

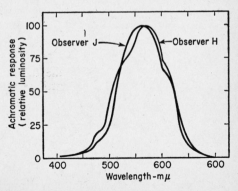

Fig. 3. *Whiteness distribution of an equal energy spectrum for two observers.*

measured by a threshold technique) that give the white-ness distribution of an equal energy spectrum for two observers (20). The induced rather than directly stimu-lated black component of the achromatic white-black re-sponse pair has this same distribution, but of opposite sign, since the strength of the black contrast response is directly related to the magnitude of either the surround-ing or the preceding whiteness or brightness.

A method for determining the spectral distributions of the paired chromatic responses is implicit in the op-ponents theory itself. Since the two members of each hue pair are mutually opponent or exclusive, then a yellow response of given strength should be exactly canceled by a stimulus that, taken alone, elicits the same magnitude of blue response, and a similar relation should hold be-tween red and green responses. Thus a null method, based on the antagonism of the two members of each hue pair, can be used to measure the spectral distributions of the chromatic responses. In brief, a wave length is first selected that evokes, say, a blue hue response. The ob-server then views, in turn, a series of spectral wave lengths that appear yellowish in hue (yellow-greens, yellow, and yellow-reds). To each of these yellow stimuli just enough of the previously selected blue stimulus is then added exactly to cancel the yellow hue without in-troducing any blueness. The observer simply reports when the test field appears neither yellow nor blue: the hue remainder that he sees may be green, neutral, or red, depending on the test wave length. Knowing the energies of the series of spectral yellow stimuli, and having de-termined experimentally the energy of the blue stimulus of fixed wave length that is required for the hue cancella-tion in each case, we can now plot the distribution of the relative magnitudes of yellow hue response evoked by the various test wave lengths. The procedure is simply re-versed to obtain the distribution of the blue component of the yellow-blue pair; that is, varying amounts of a fixed wave length of yellow hue are used to cancel the blue hue quality of a series of "blue" test wave lengths. By using a red stimulus of fixed wave length and variable energy to cancel the greens, and a green stimulus to cancel the reds, the spectral distribution of the red-green pair of chromatic responses is similarly determined.

Two sets of paired chromatic response vs. wave length functions that were measured in this way (25), together with the achromatic spectral functions shown in Fig. 3, are plotted in Fig. 4 for an equal energy spectrum. The opponent members of each hue pair have been given arbitrary positive and negative designations, to correspond with their opponent characteristics. Thus the positive values of the red-green function indicate redness, and the negative values greenness. Similarly, the positive values of the yellow-blue function indicate yellowness, and the negative values blueness.

These are the psychophysical functions that represent the spectral distributions of the three independent variables of the Hering opponent-colors theory for these two observers. They are assumed to be directly correlated with the response activity of the visual nervous tissue (retina, optic nerve, and visual centers), and should not be taken as photochemical absorption spectra, about which these data tell us nothing.

*   *   *   *   *   *   *   *   *

Ed. Note: At this point the following sections of the original article have been deleted: Brightness, Hue and Saturation; Color Mixture; Photochemical Distributions; Dependence of Hue and Saturation on Both Wave Length and Luminance; Chromatic Adaptation.

Color Anomalies and Color Blindness

When we come to consider individuals who do not have normal color vision we find that their color vision can depart from the normal in two general ways. Their color perceptions may be distorted relative to the normal, or they may exhibit specific color weaknesses or losses. Also, they may show both types of these deviant characteristics at the same time. By distorted color perceptions we mean, for example, the perceptions of the particular type of anomalous individual who has the following characteristics: he sees a distinct orange in the spectral region described normally as pure yellow or nearly so; he needs three stimuli for color mixture; he makes color matches with high precision but uses quite different proportions of the mixture stimuli than does the normal observer. An individual of this type does not seem to have lost any of the efficiency of his neural visual response processes, and it seems reasonable to assume that his color distortions

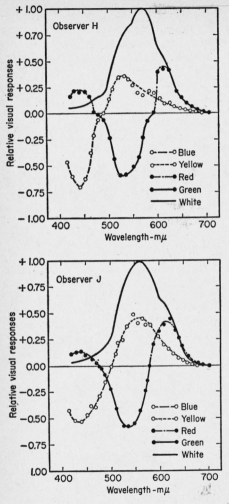

Fig. 4A and 4B. *Chromatic and achromatic response functions for equal energy spectrum for two observers.*

have their basis in the photochemical complex responsible for selective light absorption.

The particular assumptions that we have made concerning the kinds of deviation that the photosensitive materials may exhibit stem from a generalization made by Dartnall (2), on the basis of his researches concerned with the identification of visual photopigments in a variety of lower organisms. Dartnall has found that when the absorption curves of the various visual pigments are plotted as a function of the vibration frequency of the incident light (the reciprocal of the more usual wavelength specification), all the absorption curves have very nearly the same shape, and they can be made to coincide simply by shifting the curves so that they all reach an absorption maximum at the same frequency. In other words, a single template representing amount of absorption as ordinate, against frequency of radiant energy as abscissa, can be used to fit the absorption function of any visual pigment, whatever the locus of its absorption maximum. It seems reasonable to expect that this same generalization will apply to the photosensitive distributions of anomalous individuals with respect to the population of observers with normal color responses. We have consequently assumed that, in congenital abnormalities of the visual system, the normal photopigments can undergo changes that result in a uniform shift of the entire set of photosensitive distribution functions as a group along the frequency scale. These shifts are assumed to occur in either of two directions: toward higher frequencies (shorter wave lengths) resulting in the type of anomalous color vision identified as *protanomaly*, or toward lower frequencies (longer wave lengths) relative to the normal absorption loci, resulting in the second major type of anomalous color vision known as *deuteranomaly*. The amount of these displacements may also vary in different degrees of congenital anomaly.

Since the absorption of light by the photosensitive materials provides the stimulus for the neural chromatic and achromatic response systems, the visual response functions thus controlled by the deviant photosensitive materials will necessarily be altered, too, and in a systematic manner. Examples of theoretically derived anomalous response functions based on these assumptions are given in Fig. 13. The set of functions in the center block are those for the observer with normal photosensitive materials; those in the upper block are for a protanomalous

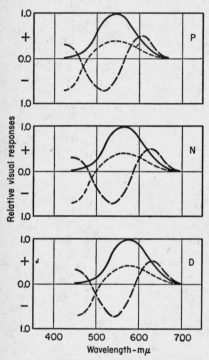

Fig. 13. *Theoretical chromatic and achromatic response functions for equal energy spectrum. For observers with protanomalous, normal, and deuteranomalous photoreceptor systems and with normal strength visual response processes.*

type whose visual pigment absorptions are assumed to be shifted toward the shorter wave lengths by an amount equal to about 15 mμ from the normal peak of about 550 mμ. This type of individual will have a luminosity function (described by the achromatic, white response function) that peaks at a shorter wave length than the normal and will show considerable loss of luminosity at the red end of the spectrum (48, Ch. 25). The spectral hues will also be altered, with a distinctly reddish yellow occurring where the normal individual sees a unique or pure yellow, whereas the protanomalous observer's pure yellow occurs at a wave length described by the normal as quite greenish. In making color matches, such as a match between 589 mμ on one side of a bipartite field and a mixture of 530 mμ and 670 mμ on the other, this observer will require a much greater proportion of 670 mμ in the mixture than will the average observer with normal color vision (27, 46). This particular match, the Rayleigh equation, is the earliest and best known diagnostic test for anomalous color vision. In this same test, the anomalous individual whose response functions are shown in the lower block in Fig. 13 will deviate from the normal in the opposite way; that is, he will require a much greater proportion of 530 mμ in the mixture for the Rayleigh equation (46). This type of anomalous individual (deuteranomalous) is assumed to have photopigment absorptions that are shifted toward the longer wave lengths, and he will see greenish-yellows where the normal sees yellow, yellows where the normal sees orange, etc. Since the neural response processes of both types of anomalies of this sort are assumed to be operating at the normal efficiency, these individuals will show high precision in making their distorted color matches, and their discriminatory capacities will also be good. As a matter of fact, anomalous individuals of this sort have understandably high confidence in their own color capability, and they are extremely resistant toward accepting the results of diagnostic tests which indicate that their visual capacities are deviant from (with the implication of "inferior to") those of the normal population (36, pp. 235-238).

Not all anomalous individuals are as fortunate as the types shown in Fig. 13, however. Many give evidence of real color weakness, in addition to distortions of the kinds already discussed (40). These color-weak individuals seem to have been deprived of some of the efficiency of the neural response processes, particularly of the red-

green opponent pair, and their systems may be represented in terms of the theory by the kinds of response
functions given as examples in Fig. 14. The visual pigments of these three types of individuals are taken to be

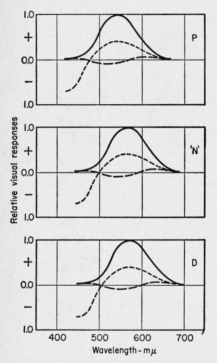

*Fig. 14. Theoretical chromatic and achromatic response func-
tions for equal energy spectrum. For observers with
protanomalous, normal, and deuteranomalous photoreceptor systems, and with impaired red-green response
processes.*

the same as those shown in the preceding figure, respectively, but the red-green paired system is reduced to one-
tenth of the normal strength. Such observers have real
losses in color discrimination in addition to possible
color distortions, and their color matches are imprecise

as well as deviant. Individuals with congenitally abnormal color systems are frequently of this general type, and cases of acquired color blindness caused by degenerative disease invariably show this kind of color weakness at some stage in the development of the neural disorder (31).

When the weaknesses become extreme, whether in congenital or acquired disorders, the red-green system

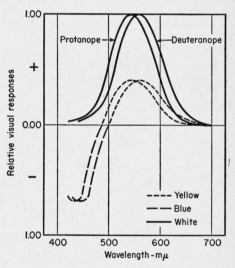

Fig. 15. Theoretical chromatic and achromatic response functions for equal energy spectrum. For observers with nonfunctioning red-green response processes.

seems to be entirely lost to normal function, and a condition of dichromasy, or so-called "color-blindness," results. That is, the visual system becomes a two-variable one, as shown in Fig. 15. Here the yellow-blue and the white-black neural systems remain intact and functioning, but there is no red-green response function. If the red-green loss occurs without changes in the visual pigments, the remaining yellow-blue and white-black response functions are like those of the normal individual;

but, since there is no red-green system, the spectrum is divided into only two hue sections for these individuals. The short wave lengths which normally vary from violet through blue and blue-green to pure green all appear as blue, but of varying saturations, with a neutral region where the normal pure green occurs. Beyond this wave length the remainder of the spectrum appears yellow, in varying saturations, out to the extreme long-wave limit of visibility. The luminosity function is the same as for the observer with normal color vision. Individuals who fit this response pattern would be classified as *deuteranopes* (29). If the visual pigments are altered, so as to produce an absorption shift toward the short wave lengths in addition to the complete red-green neural loss, then the spectrum is again divided into a short-wave blue and a long-wave yellow section, but the neutral region that divides the spectrum into the two major hues occurs at a shorter wave length than for the deuteranopes. The luminosity function is also displaced in this type of dichromasy, as it is for the anomalous individuals with similar photopigment changes, and the type of "color-blind" vision associated with this pattern is called *protanopia* (29).

These two theoretically assumed kinds of deviation from the normal system—i.e., photopigment changes and neural losses or weaknesses of the paired red-green response system—permit us to assemble a systematic picture of the many various manifestations of abnormal red-green vision that defy understanding in terms of any model of the visual system that assumes a one-to-one correspondence between light absorption in the retinal receptors and the resulting color sensations (22, 27).

Defects or losses may also occur in the yellow-blue neural response system, although such defects seem to be much more rare than the red-green defects. Again, these yellow-blue neural losses may take place either with or without changes in the photosensitive materials in the retina. Examples of the remaining red-green and white-black response functions in two types of yellow-blue blindness are given in Fig. 16. In each type of this disorder, the yellow-blue neural response function is missing, and the total gamut of colors for these individuals includes only neutral and reds and greens of various saturations. If there is no simultaneous photopigment disorder, there are two neutral points in the spectrum, one in the region where the normal sees a pure yellow, and another in the region where the normal sees a pure blue. Yellow-blue blindness of this sort is called *tetartanopia*, and only a few cases of it have been reported in the literature (e.g., 34, pp. 68-92). Slightly more common

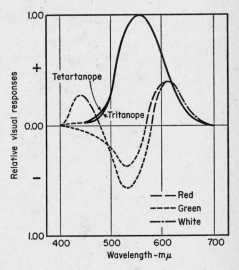

Fig. 16. *Theoretical chromatic and achromatic response functions for equal energy spectrum. For observers with nonfunctioning yellow-blue response processes.*

is the second type of yellow-blue blindness, known as *tritanopia* (49), in which not only the neural yellow-blue system is lost, but also the short-wave photopigment seems to be missing. Observers of this type have a neutral point in the normally yellow-green region of the spectrum, but there is no second neutral point, and the green hues extend into the short-wave region that appears violet to the person with normal color vision.

For all these types of deviant color vision, calculation

from the theoretical spectral response functions of discrimination curves, color mixture equations, and other psychophysical relations are in good agreement with the experimental data that are available for the various kinds of defective color systems (22, 27).

Opponents-Theory and Neurophysiology

The conceptual model for the opponent-colors theory as originally presented by Hering drew its sharpest criticism on the grounds of being bad physiology. Some of this criticism was based on an erroneous interpretation of Hering's views, an interpretation that incorrectly assigned the opponent processes to the photochemical activities in the retinal cells. Hering's own concept of mutually opponent neural processes, each capable of being activated by external stimulation, was also, however, far ahead of the knowledge of neurophysiology at the time it was proposed (16). But this concept now turns out to be perfectly consistent with the picture of neural function that is only just recently beginning to build up from electrophysiological studies of the visual neural apparatus.

It has become clear that nerves do not simply respond or fail to respond when a stimulus is presented to the appropriate end-organ. Rather, they may respond according to any of a number of quite specific patterns. For example, a nerve fiber may (a) discharge at the onset of stimulation and subsequently gradually become quiet; (b) discharge at both onset and cessation of stimulation with a quiet period in between; or (c) cease any spontaneous activity when first stimulated and during continued stimulation, but respond with a burst of electrical impulses when the stimulus ceases to act (7). The on- and off-phases of discharge are mutually inhibitory processes, they are associated with slow electrical potentials of opposite sign, and they cancel each other when the experimental conditions are so manipulated as to cause both on- and off-discharges to impinge simultaneously on the same ganglion cell (6). In Granit's opinion (6), the evidence from electrophysiology provides a "belated vindication of Hering's view" that the visual system is characterized by mutually opponent neural processes.

The concept of mutual interaction among the various

elements of the physiological field is also basic to the theory and is critical to an understanding of both areal effects and simultaneous contrast phenomena. Here again, we find the researches in electrophysiology indicating that individual nerve elements never act independently, and that visual function must be thought of in terms of the integrated action of all the units of the neural visual system (8). Hartline (9) has found that, even in the very simple Limulus eye, the discharge of impulses in any one optic nerve fiber depends not only upon the stimulus to the specific receptor unit from which that fiber arises but also upon the stimulation over the entire population of mutually interacting elements. Both excitatory and inhibitory interactions of the sort to be expected by theory have actually been demonstrated in the neural responses of the vertebrate visual system by Hartline (8), Kuffler (32), and Granit (6).

The way in which the postulated three independent systems of paired opponent processes (y-b, r-g, w-bk) are differentiated neurally is still a matter for conjecture. Hering thought it was a matter of process specificity, but was willing to use the concept of material, or structural, specificity, which he guessed would be more readily comprehended by most interested readers of his views at the time. Our own theoretical preference at this time is the conjecture that a particular color quality is more probably determined by a particular state of the nervous tissue than by activity of a particular structural element in the nervous network. Thus, we would be inclined to look for a difference between yellow-blue vs. red-green processes, rather than toward isolation of yellow-blue or red-green fibers or nerve cells.

SUMMARY

This paper has presented a summary of our progress to date in providing a quantitative formulation for the Hering opponent-colors theory, and in relating the postulated visual mechanism to specific problems of color sensation, color mixture and color discrimination; to the dependence of these functions on the physical variables of both stimulus wave length and energy level; to their further dependence on adapting and surround stimulation; and to the changes in these functions that occur in various kinds of abnormal color vision.* It is our conclusion that the opponent-colors theory serves as a fruitful working hypothesis by bringing a systematic coherence to the mass of isolated color phenomena that have been reported and subjected to quantitative experiment throughout the years. The physiological concepts basic to the theory are also shown to be consistent with recent findings in neurophysiology.

REFERENCES

1. BREWER, W. L. Fundamental response functions and binocular color matching. *J. Opt. Soc. Amer.*, 1954, 44, 207-212.
2. DARTNALL, H. J. A. The interpretation of spectral sensitivity curves. *Brit. med. Bull.*, 1953, 9, 24-30.
3. EVANS, R. M. *An introduction to color.* New York: Wiley, 1948.
4. FARNSWORTH, D. Tritanomalous vision as a threshold function. *Die Farbe*, 1955, 4, 185-196.
5. GRAHAM, C. H. Vision: III. Some neural correlations. In C. Murchison (Ed.), *A handbook of general experimental psychology.* Worcester: Clark Univer. Press, 1934. Pp. 829-879.
6. GRANIT, R. *Receptors and sensory perception.* New Haven: Yale Univer. Press, 1955.
7. HARTLINE, H. K. The response of single optic nerve fibers of the vertebrate eye to illumination of the retina. *Amer. J. Physiol.*, 1938, 121, 400-415.
8. ———. The neural mechanisms of vision. *Harvey Lectures*, 1941-42, 37, 39-68.
9. HARTLINE, H. K., WAGNER, H. G., & RATLIFF, F. Inhibition in the eye of limulus. *J. gen. Physiol.*, 1956, 39, 651-673.
10. HARTRIDGE, H. The polychromatic theory. *Documenta Ophthal.*, 1949, 3, 166-193.
11. HECHT, S. Vision: II. The nature of the photoreceptor process. In C. Murchison (Ed.), *A handbook of general experimental psychology.* Worcester: Clark Univer. Press, 1934. Pp. 704-828.

---

* For the quantitative material on normal color vision the reader is referred to the original article. Only the quantitative material on abnormal color vision is reprinted here.

12. HELSON, H. Fundamental problems in color vision. I. The principle governing changes in hue, saturation, and lightness of non-selective samples in chromatic illumination. *J. exp. Psychol.*, 1938, 23, 439-476.

13. HERING, E. *Zur Lehre vom Lichtsinne.* Berlin, 1878.

14. HERING, E. Zur Erklärung der Farbenblindheit aus der Theorie der Gegenfarben. *Lotos, Jb. f. Naturwiss.*, 1880, 1, 76-107.

15. HERING, E. Ueber Newton's Gesetz der Farbenmischung. *Lotos, Jb. f. Naturwiss.*, 1887, 7, 177-268.

16. HERING, E. *Zur Theorie der Vorgänge in der lebendigen Substanz.* Prague: 1888. (English translation by F. Welby, in *Brain*, 1897, 20, 232-258.)

17. HERING, E. *Grundzüge der Lehre vom Lichtsinn.* Berlin: Springer, 1920.

18. HOCHBERG, J. E., TRIEBEL, W., & SEAMAN, G. Color adaptation under conditions of homogeneous visual stimulation (Ganzfeld). *J. exp. Psychol.*, 1951, 41, 153-159.

19. HURVICH, L. M., & JAMESON, DOROTHEA. The binocular fusion of yellow in relation to color theories. *Science*, 1951, 114, 199-202.

20. ———. Spectral sensitivity of the fovea. I. Neutral adaptation. *J. Opt. Soc. Amer.*, 1953, 43, 485-494.

21. ———. A quantitative theoretical account of color vision. *Trans. N. Y. Acad. Sci.*, 1955, 18, 33-38.

22. ———. Some quantitative aspects of an opponent-colors theory. II. Brightness, saturation, and hue in normal and dichromatic vision. *J. Opt. Soc. Amer.*, 1955, 45, 602-616.

23. ———. Some quantitative aspect of an opponent-colors theory. IV. A psychological color specification system. *J. Opt. Soc. Amer.*, 1956, 46, 416-421.

24. ISHAK, I. G. H. Determination of the tristimulus values of the spectrum for eight Egyptian observers and one British observer. *J. Opt. Soc. Amer.*, 1952, 42, 844-849.

25. JAMESON, DOROTHEA, & HURVICH, L. M. Some quantitative aspects of an opponent-colors theory. I. Chromatic responses and spectral saturation. *J. Opt. Soc. Amer.*, 1955, 45, 546-552.

26. JAMESON, DOROTHEA, & HURVICH, L. M. Some quan-

titative aspects of an opponent-colors theory. III. Changes in brightness, saturation, and hue with chromatic adaptation. *J. Opt. Soc. Amer.*, 1956, 46, 405-415.

27. ————. Theoretical analysis of anomalous color vision. *J. Opt. Soc. Amer.*, 1956, 46, 1075-1089.

28. JONES, L. A., & LOWRY, E. M. Retinal sensibility to saturation differences. *J. Opt. Soc. Amer.*, 1926, 13, 25-34.

29. JUDD, D. B. Current views on colour blindness. *Documenta Ophthal.*, 1949, 3, 251-288.

30. ————. Basic correlates of the visual stimulus. In S. S. Stevens (Ed.), *Handbook of experimental psychology*. New York: Wiley, 1951. Pp. 811-867.

31. KÖLLNER, H. *Die Störungen des Farbensinnes.* Berlin: S. Karger, 1912.

32. KUFFLER, S. W. Discharge patterns and functional organization of mammalian retina. *J. Neurophysiol.*, 1953, 16, 37-68.

33. MACADAM, D. L. Chromatic adaptation. *J. Opt. Soc. Amer.*, 1956, 46, 500-513.

34. MÜLLER, G. E. *Darstellung und Erklärung der verschiedenen Typen der Farbenblindheit.* Göttingen: Vandenhoeck and Ruprecht, 1924.

35. PARSONS, J. H. *An introduction to the study of colour vision.* (2nd ed.) Cambridge: Cambridge Univer. Press, 1924.

36. PICKFORD, R. W. *Individual differences in colour vision.* London: Routledge and Kegan Paul, 1951.

37. PIÉRON, H. La dissociation de l'adaptation lumineuse et de l'adaptation chromatique et ses conséquences théoriques. *Année psychol.*, 1939, 40, 1-14.

38. PURDY, D. M. The Bezold-Brücke phenomenon and contours for constant hue. *Amer. J. Psychol.*, 1937, 49, 313-315.

39. RIGGS, L. A., RATLIFF, F., CORNSWEET, JANET C., & CORNSWEET, T. N. The disappearance of steadily fixated visual test objects. *J. Opt. Soc. Amer.*, 1953, 43, 495-501.

40. ROSMANIT, J. *Anleitung zur Feststellung der Farben-tüchtigkeit.* Leipzig: Deuticke, 1914.

41. TROLAND, L. T. Apparent brightness: its conditions

and properties. *Trans. Illum. Engr. Soc.*, 1916, 11, 957-966.

42. ———. *The principles of psychophysiology*. Vol. 2. *Sensation*. New York: D. Van Nostrand, 1930.

43. VON BEZOLD, W. Ueber das Gesetz der Farbenmischung und die physiologischen Grundfarben. *Ann. Phys. u. Chem.*, 1873, 150, 221-247.

44. VON KRIES, J. Die Gesichtsempfindungen. In W. Nagel (Ed.), *Handbuch der Physiologie des Menschen*. Brunswick: Vieweg, 1905. Pp. 109-282.

45. WEALE, R. A. Hue-discrimination in paracentral parts of the human retina measured at different luminance levels. *J. Physiol.*, 1951, 113, 115-122.

46. WILLIS, MARION P., & FARNSWORTH, D. Comparative evaluation of anomaloscopes. *Med. Res. Lab. Rep.* No. 190, 1952, 11, No. 7, 1-89.

47. WRIGHT, W. D., & PITT, F. H. G. The colour-vision characteristics of two trichromats. *Proc. Phys. Soc.* (London), 1935, 47, 205-217.

48. WRIGHT, W. D. *Researches on normal and defective colour vision*. St. Louis: Mosby, 1947.

49. ———. The characteristics of tritanopia. *J. Opt. Soc. Amer.*, 1952, 42, 509-521.

15

Color Defect and Color Theory

C. H. GRAHAM AND YUN HSIA

Columbia University

Different color theories differ greatly in matters of
detail, but in one thing they are in agreement: the data
of color vision cannot be accounted for in terms of the
actions of a single set of receptors or processes with
homogeneous characteristics. Rather the facts probably
require the postulation of three or more sets of elementary mechanisms, the interactions of which provide the
data of various discriminations of color. Thus, the Young-
Helmholtz theory (1, 2) presumes the existence of three
groups of receptors with different absorption characteristics, while the Hering theory (3, 4) postulates the
existence of three pairs of antagonistic processes in the
neural pathways of the visual system. Other theories
make use of other devices to account for the phenomena
of color.

Theoretical discussions of color vision have, since the
time of Young, been influenced to a great extent by
considerations of color blindness. It is interesting that
Young, at the time he put forward his account of color
in the Bakerian lecture for 1801, discussed the important
theoretical role of color blindness despite the fact that
reliable knowledge of that subject had been in existence
for less than a quarter of a century (5). The reason for
the theoretical importance of color blindness is not far
to seek. In its simplest form, as exemplified in Young's
ideas, one can think of a specific form of color deficiency

This article originally appeared in *Science*, 1958, Vol. 127,
No. 3300, pp. 675-682. Reprinted by permission of the American Association for the Advancement of Science.

as representing the loss of one of the fundamental processes from the total set that exists in normal vision. Since on this basis the eye of the color-blind can be thought of as essentially a reduced system, involving fewer than the normal number of fundamental processes, it might be expected that one could evaluate the missing process by comparing the color discriminations of a normal and color-blind eye. We shall see that such an expectation has, at best, some but certainly not complete support in what is known of the facts of color blindness.

Types of color blindness. There are several kinds of color-blind individuals classifiable in relation to normal subjects and to each other on the basis of their performances in different test situations.

Normal individuals are called *trichromats.* They can achieve a match between two mixtures of lights if one of the mixtures is a combination of a spectral color and a single color from a given unchanging set of three, called primaries, while the other mixture consists of the two remaining primaries. Conventionally, it is said that any spectral color can be matched by a mixture of three primaries, one of the primaries (the one mixed with the spectral color) having a negative value assigned to it. It is by reason of the match involving three primaries that persons with normal color vision are called trichromats.

Dichromats constitute a major class of color-blind individuals. Individuals of this group can establish a match between two mixtures that involve a spectral color and two primaries. Most dichromats are red-green blind; they "confuse" red, yellow, and green. The general class of dichromats may be subdivided into at least three types. The first class is the *protanope* whose sensitivity to wavelengths in the red end of the spectrum is greatly reduced. Another class is the *deuteranope* whose sensitivity is not deficient in the *red.* Protanopes and deuteranopes match a yellow to any amounts of red or green which will give an appropriate matching brightness (or luminance). A third type of dichromat, the *tritanope,* confuses blue and green (6).

Nothing will be said in what follows about *monochromats,* individuals who can match all wavelengths of the spectrum against any other wavelength or a white light by the proper adjustment of luminance, nor shall we elaborate on the functions of *anomalous trichromats*, people who, despite the fact that they confuse parts of the spectrum, still need three primaries to match a single wavelength.

The present experiments. This paper (7) is concerned with the visual functions of protanopes and deuteranopes, especially deuteranopes. It deals in particular with two theoretically important problems: (i) How is brightness sensitivity distributed in the spectrum for protanopes and deuteranopes? (ii) What colors do such persons *see?* On the basis of the experimental data, some proposals are made bearing on the nature of color function generally and dichromatism specifically (8).

LUMINOSITY CURVES OF DICHROMATIC
AND NORMAL SUBJECTS

The luminosity curve shows how the sensitivity of the eye varies for various wavelengths. Sensitivity (or luminosity) is measured in terms of the reciprocal of the energy required, for example, to produce threshold. Figure 1 shows the luminosity curve for the normal subject as well as the curve for the protanope and deuteranope (9). Sensitivity for the foveal cones of the normal subject is low in the blue, at a maximum in the yellow-green, and low again in the red.

The curves, as drawn by Hecht and Hsia (10), show the data of Pitt (11) for dichromats and Gibson and Tyndall (12) for normal subjects. The figure shows that, compared with normal luminosity, the curve for the protanope seems to be displaced toward the blue, whereas the deuteranope's curve is displaced a little toward the red.

It has classically been considered that protanopes show a loss of sensitivity in the red part of the spectrum. It is not so certain, however, that deuteranopes show a decrease in sensitivity in any part of the spectrum.

The curves in Fig. 1 are drawn in the traditional way of considering each luminosity function by itself and by placing the point of maximum luminosity for each at 100 percent. It will be shown that this method of repre-

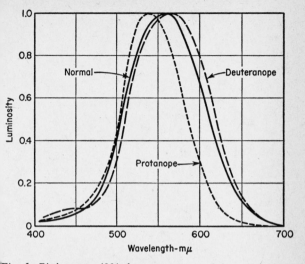

Fig. 1. Pitt's curves (11) for protanopes and deuteranopes and the data of Gibson and Tyndall (12) for normal subjects. The curves as drawn are from Hecht and Hsia (10).

senting data provides a difficulty, for it does not tell us whether the sensitivities at the 100-percent values differ in absolute value. For example, one can ask: Does the 100-percent value for the protanope refer to the same energy value as the 100-percent value for the normal subject? Arguments based upon comparisons of curves that demonstrate arbitrarily set maxima are certainly not conclusive. Specifically, the question arises whether the curves of Fig. 1 really have the same height in energy ordinates, and if not, what their relative heights are. This is the question with which we are now concerned.

If color blindness is assumed to represent the loss or inactivation of one of three receptor systems, then the loss of a receptor system should show itself in some loss of brightness in the spectrum as seen by the color-blind. One might expect, for example, each curve for a color-blind subject (Fig. 1) to have a lower maximum than the curve for normal subjects. Abney (13) drew such lowered luminosity curves for color-blind subjects. However, his reduced curves were not found from measurements but were formulated in terms of theory. Such reduced curves have only been presented once as the result of experimental research: by Hecht and Hsia (10) eleven years ago.

Because of the need for more information on this general question, we decided to investigate the relative heights of the three curves shown in Fig. 1 by measuring the actual energy thresholds of color-blind and normal subjects in different parts of the spectrum. The idea is to determine for a green portion of the spectrum the light energy required at the foveal threshold of normal persons and of color-blind persons, and to do this for different parts of the spectrum.

Selection of subjects. The testing of our subjects involved the usual "screening" tests for color-blindness, the Ishihara and Stilling plates in particular, as well as the determination of the luminances of red and green required to match a yellow on the Hecht-Shlaer (14, 15) anomaloscope. In addition, determinations were made, in the case of the protanopes and deuteranopes, of the neutral point in the spectrum—that is, the narrow wavelength band that dichromats see as white. (Normal subjects never see spectral white.) The determinations of the neutral point were made with a modified Helmholtz color mixer (Hecht and Shlaer, 14). Our final experimental groups included seven normal subjects, five protanopes, and six deuteranopes. The subjects numbered 16 men and 2 women between the ages of 20 and 35 years. (Both of the women had normal vision.)

Apparatus and procedure. Stimulating energies of light were obtained by means of a double monochromator calibrated for radiant flux. The wavelength, energy, duration, and retinal position of the stimulus could be controlled. Observations involved finding the energy threshold for the foveal cones for many narrow wavelength bands throughout the spectrum. Exposure time of each stimulus flash was 4 milliseconds.

At the beginning of each session, the subject became dark adapted for 10 minutes, a sufficient time for the cones to gain full sensitivity. Then the spectral lights were presented to him and he indicated whether or not he saw the light.

Results on normal subjects. Figure 2 gives the average log sensitivity curves for the seven normal subjects, the five protanopes, and the six deuteranopes.

The basic data of these curves are relative energies required for the cones to respond to the spectral lights at the absolute threshold; the logarithms of the reciprocals of these values (that is, log sensitivity values) are here plotted.

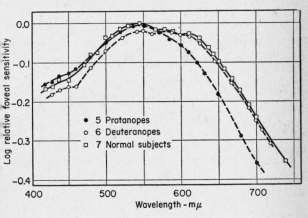

Fig. 2. The luminosity curves for normal subjects, protanopes, and deuteranobes in experiments by Hsia and Graham (9).

The peak of the average curve is arbitrarily set at zero (that is, maximum sensitivity is set at unity). It is to be noted that absolute energies may be calculated by observing that, at $\lambda = 578$ millimicrons (mμ), the average normal threshold is 3.5×10^{-8} erg. This figure amounts to about 10,000 quanta. It may be compared with a figure of about 100 quanta at the cornea obtained by Hecht, Shlaer, and Pirenne (16) for the much more sensitive peripheral retina with a small stimulus of $\lambda = 510$ mμ exposed for 1 millisecond.

It is not necessary here to labor the general fact of the

"humps" in the blue and in the orange of the normal curve, near 450 and 610 mμ. Presumably they are associated with the positions of curves representing the fundamental processes.

Results on protanopes. The average luminosity curve for five protanopes is given in the same figure. It is to be observed that the average curve for protanopes indicates a greatly increased energy requirement in the red end of the spectrum. In the blue, the energy requirement for protanopes is similar to that for normals.

Results on deuteranopes. Most writers on color blindness have not accepted the possibility that deuteranopes exhibit a loss of luminosity as contrasted with normals. Hecht and Hsia, on the basis of some determinations, maintained that a loss does occur, but their findings have met with considerable resistance, particularly by Walls and Mathews (17). Our experiment seems to demonstrate that deuteranopes usually do, in fact, lose luminosity. Five of our six cases demonstrate a loss.

The average log luminosity given by our deuteranopes is shown in Fig. 2. The luminosity for the deuteranope in the green and blue is less than the corresponding luminosity values for the normal. In the red, the values are comparable. According to our data, then, deuteranopes show a loss of luminosity in the green and blue.

General result. In general, one can say that the normal curve in this figure is a broad function that encompasses the extremes of the color-blind curves. The protanope has normal luminosity in the blue but shows loss in the red; the deuteranope shows normality in the red but a loss in the green.

Discussion. Interpretations of the data for color-blind individuals have been predominantly made in a context of trichromatic theory, developed from Young's notion that there are three receptor systems in the retina. These systems may be designated B, G, and R to indicate their properties of yielding blue, green, and red processes when they are brought into action by light. The discriminations produced by various parts of the spectrum result from the combined action of the three systems in different degrees. Thus the combined actions of the G and R system result in the seeing of yellow, while seeing white

presents the combined actions of B, G and R. The
tion of the receptors contributes brightness as well as
lor, and luminance matches show the property of
ditivity.

Young supposed that the usual dichromatic forms of
lor blindness are due to the loss of one of the three
ceptor systems. Since Young's time this interpretation
s usually been accepted in the case of protanopes:
otanopes are presumed to have lost the R receptors.

Because the evidence did not seem to support an inter-
etation of loss for the deuteranope, another sort of
count was required for this type of color defective.
his account has entailed the idea of a "transformation"
stem, as described independently by Leber (18) and
ck (19). One might think of the transformation system
representing a failure of the R and G receptors to be-
me differentiated from one another during develop-
ent. In any case, the R and G receptors are presumed
be similar insofar as absorption goes, but they have
fferent central connections. The result is that red stimu-
tes both the central R and G systems. On this basis it
uld be expected that all long wavelengths would be
lled yellow by the deuteranopic subject. Leber and
ck's idea has seemed to be in line with data on subjects
ho were reported to be normal in one eye and deuter-
opic in the other. Classically, such cases have reported
at they see yellow in the long wavelengths.

Hecht and Hsia concluded on the basis of their experi-
ent that Young's idea of a loss system was supported by
eir results. However, they were not clear about how the
ss notion could account for the color-naming responses
tributed to unilateral deuteranopes and protanopes.
he reasons for the problem are clear. How could yellow,
it is a mixture of red and green, be reported in the
sence of either red or green receptors?

)LOR DISCRIMINATIONS OF A
UNILATERALLY COLOR-BLIND SUBJECT

It is in connection with this question that we feel
rtunate in having obtained the services of a young
oman who gave color-blind discriminations with her

left eye and normal discriminations with her right ey

It would be difficult to exaggerate the importance data obtained on unilaterally color-blind subjects. N ordinary color-blind subject can tell us how the colors sees compare with those seen by a normal subject, b this is precisely what a unilaterally color-blind subject ca do. He can make a direct comparison of colors seen his color-blind and normal eyes.

Judd (20) reports that 37 cases of unilateral col blindness are described in the literature, only eight which have provided data of value to a scientific analys The last of these studies was one by Sloan and Wollac (21) in 1948. [See also a recent historical note by Berg (22).]

Our subject's first test results seemed to indicate th she was deuteranopic, and so we began our experimen with the expectation that we should gain crucial inform tion on the relation between deuteranopic luminosity lo and color naming. As our observations multiplied, w found that our subject did not give completely typic deuteranopic responses (23), particularly in hue discrim nation. However, it seems clear that she is more near classifiable as a deuteranope than as any other type color-blind individual, and we believe that her resul have a particular bearing on deuteranopia.

Luminosity curves. The luminosity curves (24) of o subject are shown in Fig. 3. The luminosity curves f her two eyes differ in luminosity values in the blue an green regions of the spectrum. Contrasted with her no mal eye, the luminosity of her color-blind eye show considerable loss. In the red end of the spectrum bot eyes have about the same sensitivity. It is possible tha as contrasted with the ordinary deuteranope, our subject luminosity loss is greater and begins at wavelengths farth into the red than is usual. In any case, she shows considerable loss in the green and blue for her colo blind eye as compared with her normal eye.

Flicker curves. We have believed it important to fin out whether or not the types of luminosity loss that occu at threshold for our subject are maintained at high in tensity levels. In order to investigate this problem w together with Eda Berger (25), have measured flick

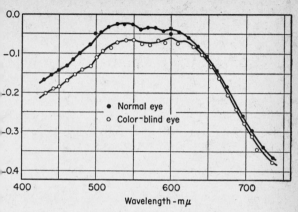

Fig. 3. Luminosity curves of a unilaterally color-blind subject. The upper curve is the curve for the normal eye; the lower one, the curve for the color-blind eye. Data of Graham and Hsia (24).

equency thresholds at various luminances of different olors.

A considerable number of curves in the normal and olor-blind eye were obtained with a number of color lters, but the general nature of the result can be demonrated by a comparison of curves for spectral regions that trichromatic person sees as blue, green, and red. The ata are shown in Fig. 4.

The curves for blue light are shown at the top of the raph. In both the normal and color-blind eye, critical icker frequency increases with intensity, the respective irves flattening out and then probably dropping at high iminance values. The positions of the two curves differ, owever. The curve for the color-blind eye is displaced ownward on the flicker axis compared with the position f the curve for the normal eye. The downward displaceient is reminiscent of the effect of decreasing the area, ence the total number of excited receptors, of a flickerig stimulus (Granit and Harper, 26).

The curves in the lower left-hand graph represent the ata for green light. The displacement of the curve for ie color-blind eye below the position of the curve for

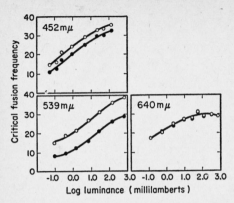

Fig. 4. Critical flicker frequency as a function of luminance for wavelengths in three different regions of the spectrum. In each graph the open circles refer to data for the normal eye, the filled circles to data for the color-blind eye. Data of Berger, Graham and Hsia (in preparation).

the normal eye is striking. In magnitude it is considerably more than was shown for blue light. In general, the displacement means that, at any given intensity, fusion frequency is higher in the normal eye than in the color-blind eye in a manner comparable to an area effect. The latter statement may be especially significant, for it means that, if critical frequency represents activated receptor units, then the type of color blindness represented by our subject is attributable to the loss of green receptors and possibly of some blue receptors also.

The story for red light is different: the same curve represents the data for the color-blind eye and the normal eye. No increased intensity requirement or fusion frequency loss for the color-blind eye is discernible in these data. No luminosity loss exists for red, even at the high intensities giving rise to critical frequencies near the maximum.

The results of the present investigation point to the conclusion that the type of color blindness represented by our subject may be characterized as a loss or inactivation of some of the receptor mechanisms that mediate sensitivity in the green and blue portions of the spectrum. Furthermore, the data show that the selective luminosity loss for our subject is not a phenomenon that exists only at cone threshold levels.

Binocular color matching. Our experiments as discussed up to the present seem to indicate that the color-blind eye of our subject, like the eyes of deuteranopes generally, shows a maximum of luminosity loss in the green region of the spectrum. What data does our subject give us on binocular color matches involving her normal and dichromatic eye? What colors does she see in her color-blind eye?

The apparatus used in the experiment on binocular color matching was essentially a mirror stereoscope arranged so as to provide slits of color in the left and right eyes, a vertical slit in the left eye and a horizontal slit in the right eye. The subject regarded the essentially monochromatic color given by the vertical slit in her dichromatic eye and simultaneously observed, in the binocular field, the monochromatic color provided by the horizontal slit in her normal eye. The subject reported that, under her conditions of viewing, the horizontal and vertical slits seemed almost to touch at the middle of the latter but did not ordinarily overlap. Wavelengths stimulating the normal eye could be changed until a monochromatic band was obtained that, in the opinion of the subject, matched the color seen by the dichromatic eye.

The results of the experiment are summarized in Fig. . In general, it seems that, in her dichromatic eye, the subject matches all wavelengths greater than her neutral point (which occurs at about 502 mμ) against a wavelength in the normal eye lying at about 570 mμ. In a word, all wavelengths greater than 502 mμ in the dichromatic eye are seen as a yellow of about 570 mμ in the normal eye. Wavelengths shorter than the neutral point in the dichromatic eye are matched in the normal eye by a blue at about 470 mμ. Thus the two sides of the spectrum below and above the neutral point are seen, respectively, as a blue equivalent to about 470 mμ and a yellow equivalent to about 570 mμ in the trichromatic

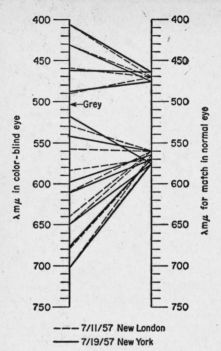

Fig. 5. Results of the experiment on binocular color matching. The wavelengths seen by the color-blind eye (lef scale) are matched by the indicated wavelengths i the normal eye (right scale).

eye (27). These results are in accord with the data o several earlier experiments on unilaterally color-blind sub jects as summarized by Judd (20).

Hue discrimination. Hue discrimination curves show how the just noticeable difference in wavelength, $\Delta\lambda$ varies with wavelength. Such data were obtained on ou unilaterally color-blind subject by means of a modifie Helmholtz color mixer (14). Careful attention was pai to making appropriate intensity adjustments so that al wavelength discriminations were obtained at the sam constant level of luminance throughout the spectrum curve was obtained on each eye of our subject. The curves are presented in Fig. 6.

In general, the curve for the normal eye does not seem to be greatly different from the usual hue discrimination curve obtained on normal individuals (28). The poorest discrimination, as shown by the largest $\Delta\lambda$, takes place in the red. Minima occur in the middle range of wavelengths; and our subject shows especially low thresholds

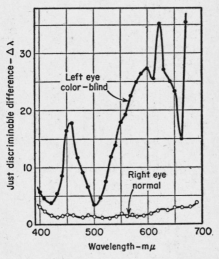

Fig. 6. *The hue discrimination of a unilaterally color-blind subject. The open circles refer to data for the normal eye; the filled circles, to data for the color-blind eye.*

in this range. It is quite clear that the normal eye of our subject does not show defective hue discrimination.

The curve for the left eye, the color-blind eye, is an entirely different function. In the violet the curve shows some insensitivity to wavelength change, but near 450 mμ it shows a great rise in $\Delta\lambda$, indicating very poor hue discrimination. Discrimination improves to a minimum threshold value near 500 mμ, in the region of the neutral point; thereafter $\Delta\lambda$ rises to very high values near 600 mμ. The behavior of hue discrimination in the spectral region from 500 to 750 mμ is similar to that found in the usual deuteranope (*11, 28*).

Color mixture. The final set of results given by our subject are her data on color mixture (*29*). One way of specifying the data of color mixture is in terms of the trichromatic coefficients. Any color, including a spectral color, can be specified in terms of three numbers. Since the numbers add to unity, the position of a color on a two-dimensional grid, the chromaticity diagram, is uniquely specified when two of the coefficients are known. Each trichromatic coefficient represents the percentage

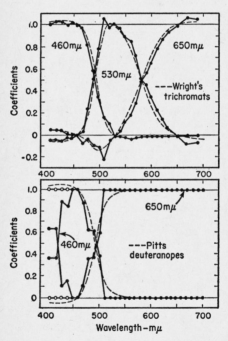

Fig. 7. *The upper curve gives the trichromatic coefficients for the normal eye of our unilaterally color-blind subject. The dashed line represents Wright's data (28,31). The lower curve gives the dichromatic coefficients for the color-blind eye of the same subject. The dashed lines represent Pitt's data (11) for deuteranopes.*

contribution of one of three primaries in providing a match for a given color. A plot of the trichromatic coefficients against wavelength results in a graph of the sort shown in the upper graph of Fig. 7. In this graph the three ordinate values at each wavelength value represent the amounts of the three primaries as percentages of the unit color (more exactly, chromaticity) of the wavelength.

The curves of the upper figure are the data for our subject's normal eye (30). In these curves, a negative trichromatic coefficient means simply that a particular primary is combined with the test wavelength to match the two remaining primaries. The curves are to be contrasted with Wright's well-known results (28, 31), on ten normal eyes as represented by the dashed lines.

Our primaries are the same as Wright's: 460, 530, and 650 mμ. The units for the red and green primaries have been so specified that they are taken to be equal at 582.5 mμ, while the green and blue primaries are equal for the match at 494 mμ. Our color-blind subject's normal eye gives, except for minor differences, the same sort of color mixture data as are represented in Wright's data. In addition, it can be stated that the relative luminance values of the primaries for matches at 582.5 and 494 mμ are comparable to those reported by Wright.

The data for our subject's color-blind eye, shown at the bottom of Fig. 7, are entirely different from the data for the normal eye. The graph shows that our subject can match any wavelength of the spectrum with a combination of two primaries, 460 and 650 mμ (the units being taken as equal at 494 mμ). The dashed line represents Pitt's data (11) on the color mixture of deuteranopes.

The open and solid circles indicate two different types of result that were obtained in the short wavelength region depending on the method used. (i) If the subject matched a given short wavelength by a mixture of the two primaries, 460 and 650 mμ, then the results are as given by the solid-circle curves. They show that, as wavelength decreases below 460 mμ, more and more of the red primary must be added to the blue primary to make a match. In a word, the colors at the blue end of the spectrum become less and less saturated as they approach

410 mμ. (ii) If mixtures were performed by Pitt's method, in which the test light is mixed with the red primary to match the mixture of red and blue primaries, the result is different, as is shown by the open circles. This result is much closer to Pitt's data than are our own results, even though our subject did not show the small degree of negative red exhibited by Pitt's subjects. It should be pointed out that our first method gives results that seem to be in line with our data on hue discrimination. (It will be remembered that our subject's dichromatic eye gave good hue discrimination thresholds in the short wavelength region of the spectrum.)

DISCUSSION

Consider now the significance of some of our data.

First, the data on color mixture demonstrate that our unilaterally color-blind subject has normal vision in her trichromatic eye and dichromatic vision in her color-blind eye. This finding means that we possess a degree of specification that was often lacking in early experiments on unilateral color blindness. We are surer of the status of our subject than were most of our predecessors. The results given by our subject on hue discrimination show the usual low thresholds characteristic of the normal eye and the high thresholds of the dichromatic eye, except, for the latter, in the blue region below 450 mμ, where discrimination is better than the usual deuteranope's.

Some important results on both our unilaterally dichromatic subject and our groups of color-blind individuals demonstrate the existence of luminosity losses in dichromatic vision. Our finding with respect to our group of protanopes is the usual one: protanopes lose luminosity in the red region of the spectrum. Our observations on a small population of deuteranopes as contrasted with normal subjects give results that are in line with some reported by Hecht and Hsia (10): five of our six deuteranopes show a loss of luminosity in the green-to-blue region of the spectrum.

A well-marked luminosity loss (over the spectral range from about 400 to 625 mμ) is shown by the dichromatic eye of our unilaterally color-blind subject. In the red region of the spectrum both of her eyes show comparable luminosity values, but in the green and blue, her color-blind eye shows a marked luminosity loss. The subject shows clear evidence of a luminosity loss over the spectral range from about 625 to about 450 mμ.

These results mean that luminosity loss is not only the usual finding for protanopes; it also exists in deuteranopes.

The second main result of our experiment concerns the findings on binocular color matches as given by our unilaterally color-blind subject. It has been demonstrated that her color-blind eye sees two hues: blue below the neutral point at about 502 mμ and yellow above it. As shown by binocular color matches, the blue she sees is equivalent, in her normal eye, to a wavelength of about 470 mμ; the yellow, to about 570 mμ.

How can these two sets of results, the one on luminosity loss and the one on binocular color matching, be reconciled within a coherent account?

What will now be presented is a statement that may have some of the advantages of the Fick-Leber hypothesis in accounting for the seeing of blue and yellow in the spectrum by protanopes and deuteranopes. It is hoped that the description can give a possible explanation of how luminosity losses can also occur in line with a transformation or "collapse" system, thereby removing what has been a shortcoming of such an account.

Let it be supposed that in deuteranopia, for example, the R fundamental curve in the upper graph of Fig. 8 (the presumed sensitivity curve for the R receptors) moves toward the short-wave part of the spectrum, with of course a change in sensitivity brought about by virtue of the transformed absorption materials. The new curve can be called R'. At the same time, the green fundamental curve G moves toward the red and becomes G'. (The blue fundamental curve will be disregarded in what follows.)

The curves in their new positions, meet certain requirements. (i) Spectral brightnesses due to R' and G' must be in the same ratio at all wavelengths in order to give yellow. (The ratio shown in Fig. 8 is taken to be unity—that is, the R' and G' curves are superimposed.) A wave-

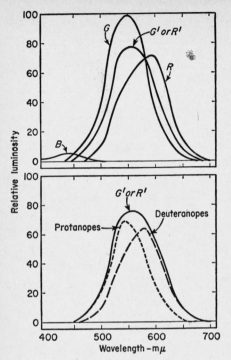

Fig. 8. Theoretical curves. The upper graph represents the transformation of the R and G curves (to superimposed R' and G' curves) to provide for the seeing of yellow by a dichromat who shows no luminosity loss. The lower graph represents the effect, for protanopes and deuteranopes of luminosity losses.

length that stimulates the now identical R' and G' substances gives yellow, for although both fundamental processes have the same absorption spectrum, they are connected centrally with the usual R and G mechanisms. (ii) The spectral brightnesses of R' and G' add to give normal sensitivities. The dichromat represented by the latter requirements shows no luminosity loss. (We have already stated that one of our deuteranopes could be so described.)

Any sensitivity loss can now be introduced, as in the lower graph of Fig. 8, by assuming a curve for deuteranopes (or protanopes for that matter) that lies beneath the normal sensitivity curve as shown in the lower graph of the figure. The sensitivity losses in this figure were computed on the basis of the group data for protanopes and deuteranopes given in Fig. 2.

The lower curves of Fig. 8 do two of the things we want them to do: (i) They account for the seeing of yellow by dichromats in the long-wave region of the spectrum, in a manner not unlike simple Fick-Leber theory (18, 19). (ii) They provide for the existence of luminosity losses in the eyes of both deuteranopes and protanopes. The implications of the account should probably be tested in further observations. Its main merit now lies in the extent to which it approximates a useful statement of how trichromatic theory can account for luminosity losses and the manner of seeing spectral colors by deuteranopes and protanopes.

SUMMARY

It is important to find answers to two questions concerning the visual discriminations of dichromatic persons, especially deuteranopes: (i) Do such persons show a loss of sensitivity to various wavelengths of the spectrum as compared with normal subjects? (ii) What colors do they see?

A number of experiments were performed on the first question.

First, luminosity curves were determined on three groups of subjects, consisting respectively of five protanopes, six deuteranopes, and seven normal individuals. As compared with normal subjects, protanopes show a loss of luminosity in the red, whereas deuteranopes show a loss in the blue-to-green region of the spectrum (See 10).

Second, we examined the luminosity curves of a subject whose right eye is classifiable (on the basis of color-mixture determinations) as normal and whose left eye is classifiable as dichromatic. (The hue discrimination curve for her dichromatic eye seemed comparable to the curve of the usual deuteranope except in the violet, where it manifested relatively good discrimination.) The luminosity function for this subject's dichromatic eye, determined by data on threshold and flicker, exhibits the same type of luminosity loss in the blue and green regions of the spectrum as was shown by our group of six deuteranopes.

Only unilaterally dichromatic subjects can tell us how colors seen by a dichromatic eye appear to a normal eye. In the color-blind eye, our unilaterally dichromatic subject sees wavelengths below and above her neutral ("grey") point (which occurs at 502 mμ) as, respectively, a blue equivalent to about 470 mμ and a yellow equivalent to about 570 mμ in her normal eye.

The results on (i) luminosity loss and (ii) the seeing of wavelengths above 502 mμ as yellow are considered theoretically. The seeing of yellow by deuteranopes and protanopes may be accounted for by an idea based on Leber-Fick transmation theory. It is proposed that the characteristic sensitivities of the red and green receptors become similar while no change takes place in their central brain connections. Losses may be introduced into the transformed sensitivity curves to indicate appropriate degrees of luminosity deficit for deuteranopes and protanopes.

REFERENCES AND NOTES

1. T. Young, "On the theory of light and colours," in *Lectures in Natural Philosophy* (Joseph Johnson, London, 1807), vol. 2, pp. 613-632.
2. H. Helmholtz, *Handbuch der physiologischen Optik* (Voss, Hamburg and Leipzig, Germany, ed. 1, 1866; ed. 2, 1896); See also, *Treatise on Physiological Optics*, English translation by J. P. C. Southall of the third German edition (1909-11) of *Handbuch der physiologischen Optik* (Opt. Soc. Am., 1924-5), vols. 1-3.
3. E. Hering, *Grundzuge der Lehre vom Lichtsinn* (Springer, Berlin, 1920).
4. L. Hurvich and D. Jameson, *J. Opt. Soc. Am.* 45, 602 (1955).
5. See D. B. Judd [*J. Opt. Soc. Am.* 33, 294 (1943)]

for references on the early history of color blindness, including Dalton's famous account (1798) and Tuberville's early statement (1684).

6. It has been proposed that a very rare type, the tetartanope, should also be listed. The tetartanope, it is claimed, also confuses blue and green, but whereas other dichromats can match a single region of the spectrum by white, the tetartanope can so match two such regions.

7. This work was supported by a contract between the Office of Naval Research and Columbia University and by a grant-in-aid from the Higgins fund of Columbia University. This article contains the essential content of a vice-presidential address given by one of us (C.H.G.) to the Psychology Section of the AAAS in December 1956. Further accounts of some of these experiments have been prepared for *Proceedings of the Symposium on Visual Problems of Color* (London: Her Majesty's Stationery Office, London, in press); *Proc. Am. Phil. Soc.* (in press); and *Symposium on Visual Mechanisms* (National Institutes of Health, Bethesda, Md., in press). Reproduction of this article, in whole or in part, is permitted for any purpose of the U.S. Government.

8. We wish to express our indebtedness to our colleagues Dr. Harry S. Sperling, Mrs. Anne H. Coulson, Dr. Eda Berger, and Mrs. Shakuntala Balaraman for many contributions of time, data, and content in the experiments here discussed.

9. Y. Hsia and C. H. Graham, *Proc. Natl. Acad. Sci. U.S.* 43, 1011 (1957)

10. S. Hecht and Y. Hsia, *J Gen. Physiol.* 31, 141 (1947).

11. F. H. G. Pitt, "Characteristics of dichromatic vision, with an appendix on anomalous trichromatic vision," *Great Britain Med. Research Council, Special Rept. Ser. No. 200* (1935).

12. K. S. Gibson and E. P. T. Tyndall, "Visibility of radiant energy," *Scientific Papers of the Bureau of Standards*, 19, No. 475, 131 (1923).

13. W. de W. Abney, *Researchers in Colour Vision* (Longmans, Green, London, 1913).

14. S. Hecht and S. Shlaer, *J. Gen. Physiol.* 20, 57 (1936); see also M. P. Willis and D. Farnsworth, *Med. Research Lab. U.S. Submarine Base, Dept. No. 190* (1952).

15. Protanopes and deuteranopes call green or red, properly adjusted for luminance, a match for yellow; hence the color-matching performance of a protanopic or deuteranopic subject on an anomaloscope (which provides standard conditions for such matches) is diagnostic of dichromatism. Protanopia seems to be indicated when a greater than usual luminance of red is required to match a yellow. When a normal luminance of red is used for the match, the subject is said to be deuteranopic.

16. S. HECHT, S. SHLAER, M. H. PIRENNE, *J. Gen. Physiol.* 25, 819 (1942).

17. G. L. WALLS and R. W. MATHEWS, "New means of studying color blindness in normal foveal color vision: with some results and their genetical implications," *Univ. Calif. Publs. Psychol. No. 7* (1952).

18. T. LEBER, *Arch. Ophthalmol.* 15, No. 3, 26 (1869).

19. A. FICK, "Die Lehre von der Lichtempfindung," in *Handbuch der Physiologie,* L. Hermann, Ed. (Vogel, Leipzig, 1879), vol. 3, pt. 1, pp. 139-234.

20. D. B. JUDD, *J. Research Natl. Bur. Standards* 41, 247 (1948).

21. L. L. SLOAN and L. WOLLACH, *J. Opt. Soc. Am.* 38, 502 (1948).

22. E. BERGER, "Some comments on the visual discriminations of unilaterally color-blind persons," in preparation.

23. It should also be mentioned that Dr. Gertrude Rand and Miss Catherine Rittler of the Laboratory of Ophthalmology, Columbia University College of Physicians and Surgeons, kindly examined our subject and concluded that, although her right eye was normal, her dichromatic eye did not fit a simple category of classical color defect. We are indebted to Dr. R. L. Pfeiffer, of the Ophthalmological Institute, Columbia University College of Physicians and Surgeons, for the ophthalmological examination of our subject. No organic disease was found.

24. C. H. GRAHAM and Y. HSIA, *Proc. Natl. Acad. Sci. U.S.* 44, 46 (1958).

25. E. BERGER, C. H. GRAHAM, Y. HSIA, "Some visual functions of a unilaterally color-blind person," in preparation.

26. On the problem of the area effect, see, for example, R. Granit and P. Harper, *Am. J. Physiol.* 95, 211 (1930).

27. A separate experiment on color naming gives data in line with the results on binocular color matching. The subject reports only two colors in her color-blind eye: blue below her neutral point at about 502 mμ, and yellow above the neutral point.

28. W. D. WRIGHT, *Researches on Normal and Defective Color Vision* (Mosby, St. Louis, Mo., 1947).

29. Some experiments on color mixture were performed at Columbia University, but the final data were obtained in collaboration with Dr. Harry G. Sperling and Mrs. Anne H. Coulson, on the Fry colorimeter at the Medical Research Laboratory of the Submarine Base, New London, Conn. A detailed account of these and other findings will be prepared as a joint report from Columbia and the Medical Research Laboratory, under Bur. Med. Project Number NM22 01 20, by C. H. Graham, H. G. Sperling, Y. Hsia, and Anne H. Coulson. We are indebted to our collaborators and to Commander Dean Farnsworth and Captain J. Vogel, officer-in-charge of the Medical Research Laboratory, for their cooperation in these experiments.

30. The relative values of the luminous units of the primaries are $l_{460} = 0.051$; $l_{530} = 1.000$, and $l_{650} = 0.814$. Matches were made by flicker photometry between the first two at 494 mμ, and for the second and third, at 582.5 mμ. The luminous units are within the range reported by Wright (28) for his normal subjects. The experiments were done with retinal illuminances of test wavelengths equal in all cases to 500 trolands as established by flicker photometry.

31. W. D. WRIGHT, *Trans. Opt. Soc. (London)* 30, 141 (1928-29).

16

Experiments in Color Vision

Edwin H. Land

From childhood onward we enjoy the richness of color in the world around us, fascinated by the questions: "How do we see color? How do you know you see the same color I do? Why do colors sometimes mix to give quite different colors?" Since 1660, when Isaac Newton discovered the properties of the visible spectrum, we have slowly been learning the answers; and we are finding that the beauty of the outer world is fully matched by the technical beauty of the mechanisms whereby the eye sees color.

No student of color vision can fail to be awed by the sensitive discernment with which the eye responds to the variety of stimuli it receives. Recently my colleagues and I have learned that this mechanism is far more wonderful than had been thought. The eye makes distinctions of amazing subtlety. It does not need nearly so much information as actually flows to it from the everyday world. It can build colored worlds of its own out of informative materials that have always been supposed to be inherently drab and colorless.

Perhaps the best way to begin the story is to consider two sets of experiments. The first is the great original work of Newton, which set the stage for virtually all research in color vision since that time. The second is an apparently trivial modification that reverses some of his basic conclusions.

This article originally appeared in the *Scientific American*, May, 1959, pp. 84-99. The photographs have not been included in this book. Reprinted by permission.

As is so often the case with truly revolutionary insights, the simplicity of Newton's discovery causes one to wonder why no one before him had made it. He passed a narrow beam of sunlight through a prism and found that it fanned out into the band of colors we know as the visible spectrum: red, orange, yellow, green, blue, indigo and violet. When he reversed the process, gathering the beam together with a second prism, the colors vanished and white light reappeared. Next he tried recombining only parts of the spectrum, inserting a slotted board to cut off all but certain selected bands [*see diagram on page 167*]. When he combined two such bands of color, letting the rays mix on a screen, a third color appeared, generally one matching a color lying between the bands in the spectrum.

Let us repeat this last experiment, placing the openings in the board just inside the ends of the narrow yellow band in the spectrum. When these two yellow beams strike the screen, they combine, as Newton observed, to produce yellow.

Now for our modification. In front of the slits we place a pair of black-and-white photographic transparencies. Each shows the same scene: a collection of variously colored objects. There is, of course, no color in the photographs. There are simply lighter and darker areas, formed by black silver grains on transparent celluloid. A glance at the two shows that they are not absolutely identical. Some of the objects in the scene are represented by areas which are lighter in the first photograph than in the second. Others are darker in the first and lighter in the second. But all that either photograph can do is to pass more or less of the light falling on its different regions.

The yellow beams pass through these transparencies and fall on the screen. But now they are not yellow! Somehow, when they are combined in an image, they are no longer restricted to producing their spectral color. On the screen we see a group of objects whose colors, though pale and unsaturated, are distinctly red, gray, yellow, orange, green, blue, black, brown and white. In this experiment we are forced to the astonishing conclusion that the rays are not in themselves color-making. Rather

they are bearers of information that the eye use
to assign appropriate colors to various objects in an
image.

THE OLD THEORY

This conclusion is diametrically opposed to the main
line of development of color theory, which flows from
Newton's experiments. He and his successors, notably
Thomas Young, James Clerk Maxwell and Hermann von
Helmholtz, were fascinated by the problem of simple
colors and the sensations that could be produced by com
pounding them. Newton himself developed quite good
rules for predicting the colors that would be seen when
various spectral rays were mixed to form a spot of light
on a screen. These rules can be summarized in geo
metrical diagrams, one of the oldest of which is the color
triangle [see diagram at top of page 181]. On modern
versions of it we can read off the result of combining so
many parts of color A with so many of color B.

Once it was discovered that light is a wave motion, the
classical investigations of color acquired a deeply satisfy
ing logical basis. The order of colors in the spectrum fol
lows wavelength, the longest visible wavelength falling at
the red end of the spectrum and the shortest at the violet
end. A pure color would be a single wavelength; com
pound colors would be mixtures of pure colors.

In trying to match colors by mixing spectral stimuli
Maxwell and Helmholtz found that three different wave
lengths were enough to effect all matches, and that those
wavelengths had to be chosen from the red, green and
blue bands of the spectrum. Accordingly red, green and
blue came to be called the primary colors. On the basis
of this evidence they proposed a three-color theory of
color vision. We need not go into the details here. The
central idea is that the eye responds to three different
kinds of vibration, and that all color sensation is the
result of stimulating the three responses in varying de
grees of strength. Thus it has become an article of faith
in standard theory that the color seen at any point in a
field of view depends on what wavelengths are issuing

from that point and upon their relative strengths or intensities.

Now, as we have seen in our modification of Newton's experiment, the light at any point on the screen was composed of only two "yellow" wavelengths, yet the image was fully colored. And, as we shall see later, the colors in images will be remarkably stable even when the over-all relative strengths or intensities of the two wavelengths are varied.

NATURAL IMAGES

Is something "wrong" with classical theory? This long line of great investigators cannot have been mistaken. The answer is that their work had very little to do with color as we normally see it. They dealt with spots of light, and particularly with pairs of spots, trying to match one to another. The conclusions they reached were then tacitly assumed to apply to all of color sensation. This assumption runs very deep, and has permeated all our teaching, except for that of a few investigators like E. Hering, C. Hess and the contemporary workers Dorothea Jameson and Leo M. Hurvich (who have studied the effect produced on a colored spot by a colored surround).

The study of color vision under natural conditions in complete images (as opposed to spots in surrounds) is thus an unexplored territory. We have been working in this territory—the natural-image situation, as we call it —for the past five years. In the rest of this article I shall describe some of the surprises we have encountered.

To form the image in our modification of Newton's experiment we needed two sets of elements: a pair of different photographs of the same scene, and a pair of different wavelengths for illuminating them. It is possible to make the pictures different by tinkering in the laboratory, arbitrarily varying the darkness of their different areas. But, as every photographer will have recognized at this point, a simple way to produce the two pictures is to make "color separations," that is, to photograph the scene through two filters that pass different bands of wavelengths. In this way the film is systematically exposed to longer wavelengths coming from the scene in one case, and to shorter wavelengths in the other. In our investigations we usually use a red filter for the longer wavelengths and a green filter for the shorter.

Now when we illuminate the transparencies with practically any pair of wavelengths and superimpose the images, we obtain a colored image. If we send the longer of the two through the long-wave photograph and the shorter through the short-wave photograph, we obtain most or all of the colors in the original scene and in their proper places. If we reverse the process, the colors reverse, reds showing up as blue-greens and so on.

LONG WAVELENGTHS V. SHORT

It appears, therefore, that colors in images arise not from the choice of wavelength but from the interplay of longer and shorter wavelengths over the entire scene. Let us now test this preliminary hypothesis by some further experiments.

There are several more convenient ways to combine images than in the arrangement of Newton's experiment. One of the simplest is to place the transparencies in two ordinary projectors, using filters to determine the illuminating wavelengths.

When we work with filters, we are not using single wavelengths, but rather bands of wavelengths; the bands have more or less width depending on the characteristics of each filter. It turns out that the width of the band makes little difference. The only requirement is that the long-wavelength photograph, or, as we call it, the "long record," should be illuminated by the longer bad and the "short record" by the shorter band. Indeed, one of the bands may be as wide as the entire visible spectrum. In other words, it may be white light.

One advantage of this arrangement is that an observer can test the truth of our hypothesis in a simple and dramatic way. According to classical theory the combination of red and white can result in nothing but pink. With no photograph in either projector, and with a red filter held in front of one of them, the screen is indeed pink. Now the transparencies are dropped into place and the view changes instantly to one of full, vivid color. If the red filter is taken away, the color disappears and we see a black-and-white picture. When the filter is put back, the colors spring forth again.

An incidental advantage in using red for the long record and white for the short lies in the fact that the colors produced look about the same to color film as they do to the eye. Thus the image can be photographed directly. With more restricted bands of wavelengths the film, which does not have the new-found versatility of the eye, cannot respond as the eye does, and reproductions must be prepared artificially.

The projectors afford a simple way of testing another

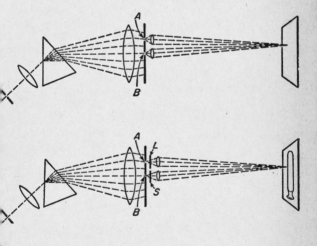

NEWTON'S EXPERIMENT *in mixing spectral colors is shown schematically at top; the author's modification of the experiment, in which a pair of black-and-white transparencies is inserted in the beams, is diagrammed at bottom. When slits* a *and* b *are both in the yellow band of the spectrum, Newton's arrangement produces a spot of yellow on the screen. The image at bottom contains a gamut of color. The letters* l *and* s *in this diagram and others in this article refer, respectively, to the long record and the short record.*

variable: brightness. By placing polarizing filters in front of the projector's lenses we can vary the amount of light reaching the screen from each source. With no transparencies in the projector, but with the red filter still over one lens, the screen displays a full range of pinks, from red to white, as the strengths of the two beams are changed. When the photographs are in place, the colors

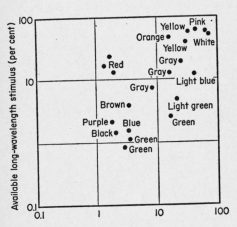

AVAILABLE SHORT-WAVELENGTH STIMULUS
(PER CENT)

COORDINATE SYSTEM *predicts colors in natural images.
Axes are dimensionless, each measuring illumination at every
point as a percentage of the maximum that could be there.*

of the image on the screen hold fast over a very considerable range of relative intensities.

Let us pause for a moment to consider the implications of this last demonstration. Remember that the photographs are nothing but pieces of celluloid treated to pass more light in some places than in others. All they can do to the red and white beams is to change relative intensities from point to point. In doing so they stimulate a complete gamut of color. Yet when we vary the relative intensities of the beams over the whole field of view, the colors stay constant. Evidently, even though the eye needs different brightness ratios, distributed over various parts of the image, to perceive color, the ratios that the eye is interested in are not simple arithmetic ones. Somehow they involve the entire field of view. Just how they involve it we shall see a little later.

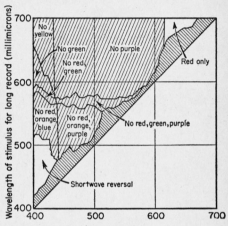

WAVELENGTH OF STIMULUS FOR SHORT RECORD (MILLIMICRONS)

COLOR MAP *shows limits on color obtainable with different pairs of wavelengths. The gray area is an achromatic region in which wavelengths are too close together to produce any kind of color. In the region marked "short-wave reversal" the colors are normal, but the short wavelengths act as the stimulus for the long record and the long wavelengths as the stimulus for the short record. The blank area below the diagonal is a region of reversed color obtained by illuminating the short record with long wavelengths and* vice versa.

The dual-projector system is convenient, but it is not a precision instrument. The wavelengths it can provide are limited by the characteristics of available filters. Narrow band-width filters may be used, but they seriously restrict the quantity of light. My colleague David Grey has therefore designed for me a dual image-illuminating monochromator [*see illustration on page 179*]. This instrument contains a pair of spectroscopes which allow us to light our transparencies with bands as narrow as we choose and of precisely known wavelength. By blocking off the spectroscopes and using filters, we can also obtain white light or broad bands. The two images are combined by means of a small, semitransparent mirror; light from one record passes through the mirror, and light from the other is reflected from its top surface. The intensity of each light source can be closely controlled.

With the dual monochromator we have confirmed our broad hypothesis: Color in natural images depends on a varying balance between longer and shorter wavelengths over the visual field. We have also been able to mark out the limits within which color vision operates. It turns out that there must be a certain minimum separation between the long-record wavelength and the short. This minimum is different for different parts of the spectrum. Any pair of wavelengths that are far enough apart (and the minimum distance is astonishingly small) will produce grays and white, as well as a gamut of colors extending well beyond that expected classically from the stimulating wavelengths. Many combinations of wavelengths produce the full gamut of spectral colors, plus the nonspectral color sensations such as brown and purple. All this information has been summarized in a color map showing the limitations on the sensations produced by different pairs of wavelengths [*see the illustration on preceding page*]. We have also investigated the limits

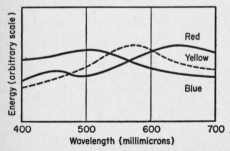

PIGMENTS IN OUR WORLD *have broad reflection characteristics. Each pigment reflects some energy from wavelengths across the visible spectrum (400 to 700 millimicrons).*

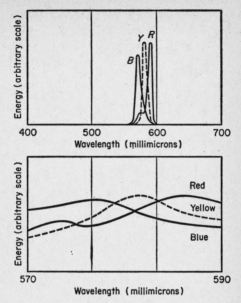

PIGMENTS IN AN IMAGINARY WORLD, *whose available light is limited to a band of wavelengths extending only from about 570 millimicrons to 590 millimicrons, would have to be much more sharply selective. Upper curves show reflection curves of pigments which would give full color in such a world. Lower curves represent the same curves stretched out so that the 570-590 band covers the same width as the 400-700 band of the visible spectrum.*

on relative brightness. With some pairs the colors are maintained over enormous ranges of brightness; with others they begin to break down with smaller changes. Again, the result depends on the wavelengths we are using. A table showing the stability of various colors for a sample pair of wavelengths appears on page 182.

A NEW COORDINATE SYSTEM

The color map tells us what we will *not* see when we combine a pair of images at various wavelengths. Can we now make a positive prediction? Given a pair of records of the same scene, and a pair of wave bands with which to illuminate them, what color will appear at each specific point on the combined image? In other words, we want a set of rules that will do for images what the color triangle does for color-matching experiments (and what most of us have mistakenly supposed it does for images as well).

We have formed a new coordinate system that does for the first time predict the colors that will be seen in natural images. Perhaps the best way to approach it is through an actual experiment. Let us set up the dual projector (or the monochromator) for any pair of "long" and "short" bands, say red and white, that can produce full color. We know that local variations in the relative brightness of the two records must somehow give rise to the color. Yet we have also found that changing all the brightness ratios in a systematic way, for example by cutting down the total light from the red projector, has no effect. Therefore we look for a way of describing the brightness in terms that are independent of the total light available in either image.

This can be done as follows: We turn on the "long" projector alone, setting its brightness at any level. Now we find the spot on the red image corresponding to the point at which the long black-and-white record lets through the most light. We measure the intensity at that point and call it 100 per cent. It tells us the maximum available energy for the long waves. Next we measure the intensity of the light all over the rest of the red image, marking down for each point the red intensity as a per cent of the maximum available. Then we turn off the "long" projector, turn on the "short" one and follow the same procedure for the short wavelengths (in this case the full spectral band). Now we draw up a two-dimensional graph [*top of page 168*], plotting the percentage of available long wavelengths on one axis and the percentage of available short wavelengths on the other. Every point on the image can be located somewhere on this graph. Each time we plot a point, we note next to it the color it had on the image.

What emerges is a map of points, each associated with

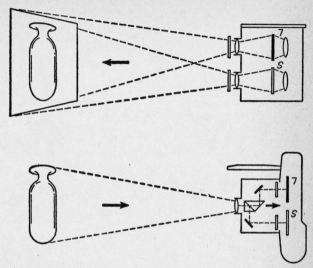

LONG AND SHORT RECORDS *are prepared by photographing a scene with the dual camera diagrammed at top. Small
open rectangles represent colored filters; the filter in front of
the long record is red and the one in front of the short record
is green. A composite image is formed by superimposing long
and short records (labeled 1 and s on a screen by means of a
dual projector bottom).*

a color. When it is finished, we can see that the map is
divided into two sections by the 45-degree line running
from lower left to upper right. This is the line of gray
points. If we had put the same transparency in each projector, all the points would fall on the gray line, since the
percentage of available light would be the same at every
point on the image for both projectors. The other colors
arrange themselves in a systematic way about the 45-
degree line. Warm colors are above it; cool colors are
below. Thus it seems that the important visual scale is
not the Newtonian spectrum. For all its beauty the spectrum is simply the accidental consequence of arranging
stimuli in order of wavelength. The significant scale for
images runs from warm colors through neutral colors to
cool colors.

Repeating our experiment with different illuminating wavelengths or bands, we find that for every pair that produces full color the position of the colors on the coordinate graph remains the same. Thus we have the rule we were looking for, a rule that tells us in advance what color we shall find at any point in an image. We can take any pair of transparencies and measure their percentage of transmission in various regions of the picture. Then, before projecting them, we can predict the colors these areas will have. We will be right provided that the illuminating wavelengths are capable of stimulating all the colors. In cases where they are not, we must change the coordinate map accordingly. Thus the full set of rules consists of a group of coordinate color plots, one for each section of the color map at the bottom of page 169.

Note that each coordinate system is itself dimensionless. The axes do not measure wavelength, brightness or any other physical unit. They express a ratio of intensities at a single wavelength or for a broad band of wavelengths. The axes have another interesting property: they are stretchable. Suppose we superimpose two identical long-wavelength photographs in the slide holder of the "long" projector and leave a single short-wavelength photograph in the holder of the "short" projector. We find that this combination still does not alter the colors on the screen. What sort of change have we made? Every point in the long record that transmitted ½ of the available light now transmits ¼, points that transmitted ⅕ now transmit 1/25 and so on. On the logarithmic scale of our graph this corresponds to stretching the long-record axis to twice its former length. The 45-degree line now shifts to a new direction, but all the color points shift with it, maintaining their relative positions [see diagram on page 177].

RANDOMNESS

Our studies of the coordinate graph have uncovered another interesting and subtle relationship. As we plotted graphs for various experiments we began to suspect that any arrangement which yielded points falling on a straight line, or even on a simple smooth curve, would be color-

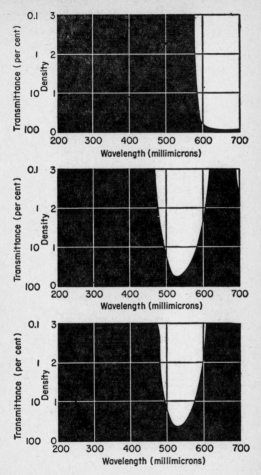

WAVELENGTHS PASSED BY FILTERS used in various experiments described by the author are shown in these curves. At top is the transmittance curve for the red filter used in photographing long record; below it is transmittance curve of green filter for preparing short record. At bottom is curve for the green filter used in the sodium-viewer experiment.

less. To test this idea we tried putting a negative photo graph in one projector and a positive of that negative in the other. Such a pair of images will plot as a straight line running at right angles to the 45-degree gray line. The image is indeed virtually colorless, showing only the two "colors" of the stimuli involved in projection and a trace of their Newtonian mixture.

If an image is to be fully colored, its coordinate graph must contain points distributed two-dimensionally over a considerable area. But even this is not enough. The points must fall on the graph in a somewhat random manner, as they do in the plot of any natural scene. This require ment can be demonstrated in a very striking experiment. Suppose we put a "wedge" filter in the slide holder of the red projector. The effect of the filter is to change the intensity of the beam continuously from left to right. That is, when the red projector is on and the white pro jector off, the left side of the screen is red and the right side is dark, with gradations in between. Now we place a similar wedge, but vertically, in the white projector so that the top of the screen is white and the bottom is dark. With both projectors turned on we now have an infinite variety of red-to-white ratios on the screen, duplicating all those that could possibly occur in a colored image. However, they are arranged in a strictly ordered progres sion. There is no randomness. And on the screen there is no color—only a graded pink wash.

To repeat, then, the colors in a natural image are de termined by the relative balance of long and short wave lengths over the entire scene, assuming that the relation ship changes in a somewhat random way from point to point. Within broad limits, the actual values of the wave lengths make no difference, nor does the over-all available brightness of each.

The independence of wavelength and color suggests that the eye is an amazingly versatile instrument. Not only is it adapted to see color in the world of light in which it has actually evolved, but also it can respond with a full range of sensation in much more limited worlds. A dramatic proof of this is provided by another series of experiments.

COLOR WORLDS

In these we use a pair of viewing boxes that superimpose fairly large images by means of semitransparent mirrors [*see diagram at bottom of page 183*]. Each box contains tungsten lamps, which produce white light, to

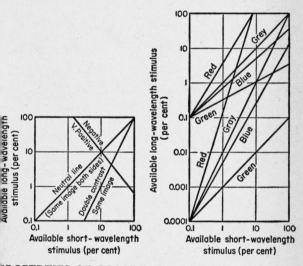

PROPERTIES OF COORDINATE SYSTEM *are illustrated in these diagrams. At left are the graphs of experimental situations which do not produce a gamut of color in the image. Such situations appear to graph as straight lines. At right the axes are shown to be stretchable. When gray line dividing warm and cool colors is displaced, colors move but maintain their relative positions.*

illuminate one record and a sodium lamp to illuminate the other. We turn on one viewer, inserting the long and short transparencies and placing a red filter over the tungsten lamp. The composite image is fully colored, containing greens and blues, although the shortest wavelength coming from the mirror lies in the yellow part of the spectrum. Now we turn on the second viewer, inserting a green filter over the white light-source. Again the image contains a gamut of color, including red. The observer can see the images in both viewers at once—each showing the same range of color, but representing different visual worlds. In the first the sodium light (with a wavelength of 589 millimicrons) serves as the shortest available wavelength and helps to stimulate the green and blue. In the second it is the longest wavelength and stimulates red. If the observer stands back far enough from the viewer, he can also see the "natural" colors in the room around him. Here then is a third world in which yellow is "really" yellow.

Another way to use the green filter in the second sodium viewer is to hold it up to the eye instead of placing it in front of the tungsten lamps. This filter passes both the sodium wavelength and the green band [see bottom graph on page 175]. When he looks around the room, the observer sees red objects as black and the rest of the colors as washed-out green. But when he looks at the picture in the second viewing box, he sees it quite full of color, including red.

The color worlds of the viewers are produced by pictures. Could we make physical models of these worlds, populating them with real objects which would show the same colors as the images in the viewers under the same conditions of illumination? We could if only we had the proper pigments. The pigments in the world around us are the best we have been able to find that look colored in our lighting: a spectrum of visible wavelengths from 400 to 700 millimicrons. Each of these pigments reflects a broad band of wavelengths, and its peak is not sharp [see diagram on page 170].

Thus our coloring materials do not distinguish clearly between wavelengths that are fairly close together. If we could find pigments with much narrower response curves, we would suspect that these might provide full color in a more restricted world of light—a world, for example, lighted by the wavelengths that pass through the green filter. In the absence of such coloring materials, we might content ourselves with creating this world photographically, if we could show that this is possible. A moment's study of the diagrams on page 171 will show the exciting

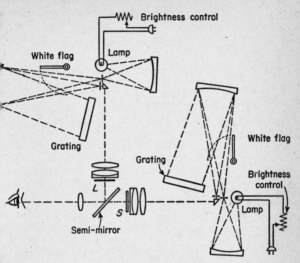

DUAL MONOCHROMATOR *used in experiments described
 this article is diagrammed. Very narrow bands of wavelengths
 om any part of the visible spectrum are produced by the two
 atings. White flags can be inserted to give white light. Narrow
 ctangles marked* l *and* s *represent the black-and-white trans-
 rencies that serve as the long record and the short record
 spectively.*

ct that a two-color separation photograph in a world of
 y band-width is the same as a two-color photograph in
 world of any other bandwidth—including our own,
 ovided that we postulate that a correctly proportioned
 ange in the absorption bands of the pigments goes
 ong with a change in the band-width of the world.
 herefore we can use our regular long and short pictures,
 ken through the red and green filters, to transport our-
 ves into new worlds with their new and appropriately
 rrow pigments.

HE VISUAL MECHANISM

The sodium-viewer demonstration suggests an impor-
 nt consideration that we have not previously men-

tioned, although it is implicit in what has already bee
said. If the eye perceives color by comparing longer a
shorter wavelengths, it must establish a balance point
fulcrum somewhere in between, so that all wavelength
on one side of it are taken as long and all on the oth
side as short. From the evidence of the viewer we can s
that the fulcrum must shift, making sodium light long
one case and short in the other.

Where is the fulcrum in the ordinary, sunlit worl
Experiments on a large number of subjects indicate th
it is at a wavelength of 588 millimicrons. When we u
this wavelength in one part of the dual monochromat
and white light in the other, the image is nearly colorles
With a wavelength shorter than 588 millimicrons, whi
serves as the longer stimulus in producing color; with
wavelength longer than 588 millimicrons, white becom
the short record.

From the dual-image experiments we learn that wh
the eye needs to see color is information about the lo
and short wavelengths in the scene it is viewing. It mak
little difference on what particular bands the messag
come in. The situation is somewhat similar to that
broadcasting: The same information can be conveyed
any of a number of different stations, using different ca
rier frequencies. But a radio must be tuned to the rig
frequency. Our eyes are always ready to receive at a
frequency in the visible spectrum. And they have th
miraculous ability to distinguish the longer record fro
the shorter, whatever the frequencies and the ban
widths. Somehow they establish a fulcrum and divide t
incoming carrier waves into longs and shorts around th
point.

In our experiments we provide a single photograp
averaging all the long wavelengths and a single phot
graph averaging all the short. What happens in the re
world, where the eyes receive a continuous band of wav
lengths? We are speculating about the possibility th
these wavelengths register on the retina as a large numb
of individual color-separation "photographs," far mo
than the three that Maxwell thought necessary and fa
more than the two that we have shown can do so we
The eye-brain computer establishes a fulcrum wavelengt

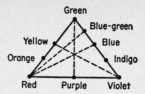

COLOR TRIANGLE of classical theory is shown in an early schematic form. Points of intersection of lines represent colors obtained by mixing spectral wavelengths in amounts proportional to distances from sides of triangle. Central point is equal mixture of primaries and is therefore white.

then it averages together all the photographs on the long side of the fulcrum and all those on the short side. The two averaged pictures are compared, as real photographic images are compared in accordance with our coordinate system.

Finally I should like to make clear that, although our

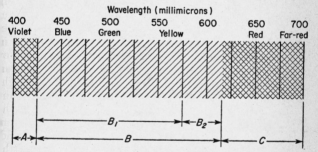

WAVELENGTH AND COLOR are independent of each other, except for the long-short relationship. This diagram shows the roles that various wavelengths can play. Those in the interval a can serve only as the short-record stimulus; those in b may be either long or short; those in c can only be long. If the wavelengths in b_1 are used as short-record stimuli, they will combine with a longer wavelength to produce the full gamut of color. If they are used as long-record stimuli, they will produce a more limited range. Wavelengths in b_2 will produce full color, serving as the stimuli for either the long record or for the short record. When both stimuli come from between 405 and 520 millimicrons, "short-wave reversal" occurs (see color map on page 169).

experiments deal with two photographs and our co-ordinate system is two-dimensional, we have not been describing a two-color theory of vision. When we use a band of wavelengths for either or both of the records, we have light of many wavelengths coming from each point on the screen. And if classical three-color theory holds, it should describe the color of each of these points. This, as we have seen, it completely fails to do. It is true, however, that our experiments deal with two packages of information. We have demonstrated that the eye can do almost everything it needs to do with these two packages. The significance of what a third package will add is far from obvious. We are building a triple image-illuminating monochromator to find out.

A third picture may provide better information at the photographic level or an additional and useful interaction with the stimuli from two images. However, there is not

Colors Seen	Range Over Which Seen	Variation in Color Over This Range
Gray	200 to 1	Little Variation
Brown	100 to 1	Yellow-Brown to Dark Brown
White	100 to 1	Yellowish-White to Bluish-White
Yellow	30 to 1	Yellow to Off-White
Yellow-Green	30 to 1	Yellow-Green to Yellow Orange
Blue	10 to 1	Blue-Violet to Blue Green
Green	6 to 1	Blue-Green to Gray-Green
Red	5 to 1	Dark Red to Dark Orange-Red
Orange	5 to 1	Yellow to Red-Orange

Limits of Stability of colors under variation in relative brightness of a sample pair of long and short stimuli are summarized in this typical chart. Second column shows the mechanism ratio (changing the brightness of either or both of the stimuli) for which color at left is recognizable. Pair of stimuli used was 450 millimicrons and 575 millimicrons.

very big gap in the sensation scale to be filled by the
third picture. In a given image a particular combination
of two stimuli might not provide an electrically intense
blue or a delicately yellowish green, but it is still likely to
provide more than enough for the animal to live with.
Nevertheless we do expect that the richness of many
colors will be increased by the interplay of a third stimulus. Whatever we learn by adding a third picture, the
visual process will remain an amazing one from the
evolutionary point of view. Why has a system that can
work so well with two packages of information evolved

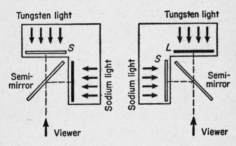

SODIUM-VIEWING BOXES *diagrammed schematically. Each
of these instruments produces a large composite image by
means of the semitransparent mirror. Tungsten light is white,
and is restricted to narrower bands of wavelengths by means of
colored filters.*

to work better with three? And who knows whether it will
not work better still with four, or five or more?

What does the eye itself do in the everyday world of
the full spectrum? Does it make only two averages? Or
does it put to better use the new ability we have discovered—the ability to distinguish sharply between
images at closely spaced wavelengths? Perhaps it creates
many sets of averages instead of just two or three.

Even if more than two information channels are used,
we feel that the big jump is obviously from one to two.
Most of the capability of our eyes comes into play here.
And whatever may be added by more channels, the basic
concept will remain. Color in the natural image depends
on the random interplay of longer and shorter wavelengths over the total visual field.

17

Vision

CHARLES E. OSGOOD

VISUAL QUALITY

The psychology of vision is replete with conflicting theories, designed as explanations of how the nervous system mediates the known relations between physical light stimulus and psychological color experience. Theories are limited only by existing knowledge of how, in general, the sensory nervous system works and by an accumulated mass of indirect evidence, but they tend to stray beyond even these boundaries. Impetus to theory building came from the discovery that all hue experiences could be duplicated by appropriate mixtures of only three primaries; this seemed to limit the complexity of the problem—perhaps only three receptor types were sufficient to explain color vision.

Could it be done with less than three? At the extreme we would have a *single receptor theory*, with hue dependent upon the frequency of impulses in the visual nerve tract (in a manner analogous to the volley theory of pitch) and brightness dependent upon total frequency per unit time. This has seldom been seriously proposed (however, see Troland, 1921; Fry, 1945): the notion runs into flat contradiction of the law of specific energies

We end this volume with an overview of the problem, excerpted from a standard text in experimental psychology. It puts the theories and problems of color vision in perspective, drawing them together so that one can see how the various parts fit and what theories are best at handling what kinds of data. The selection is from *Method and Theory in Experimental Psychology* by Charles E. Osgood. Copyright 1953 by Oxford University Press, Inc. Reprinted by permission.

(a difficulty shared with respectable theories, by the way), fails to provide a ready explanation of color mixture and saturation, and certainly doesn't explain how we can have different types of color blindness. Is the other extreme, an *N-receptor theory*, feasible? This notion, like the place theory of hearing, would require as many different types of receptors as there are discriminable hues, and there are some 128 of them (cf. Troland, 1934). This would seem to place an impossible burden upon retinal chemistry; it is difficult to conceive of anything approaching this number of different light-sensitive substances. Furthermore, since vision (unlike audition) includes a spatial dimension, each small area of the retina yielding full color discrimination would have to include full replication of all cone types.

All contemporary theories represent a compromise between these extremes, specifying some *limited* number of receptor types that vary in their rate of discharge with the wave length of light. The classic Young-Helmholtz theory, deriving its *raison d'être* from the facts of color mixture, specifies three types of cones. Despite numerous weaknesses, this is still the dominant point of view. Other theories have appeared from time to time, but they are chiefly criticisms of the Young-Helmholtz position. We shall first describe the classic theory and then evaluate it against many kinds of experimental evidence, taking cognizance of competing theories.

THE YOUNG-HELMHOLTZ THEORY

By the time Thomas Young (1801) was mulling over these problems, a century after Newton, it was well established that light is infinitely divisible. Young, like present-day theorists, found it difficult to conceive of each sensitive point in the retina containing "an infinite number of particles, each capable of vibrating in perfect unison with every possible undulation." His ingenious suggestion was that there are only three kinds of fibers corresponding to three primary colors. Although Young never made the implications of this theory explicit, it follows that if anything other than the primaries are to be sensed (a) each fiber must respond in varying degrees to all

wave lengths and (b) the messages carried by the three
types of fibers must be fused or interpreted, presumably
in the brain. After reposing quietly in the Philosophical
Transactions of the Royal Society for nearly fifty years,
these ideas were discovered, more or less simultaneously,
by both Maxwell and Helmholtz, who brought them
into close alignment with the facts of color mixture.

The Young-Helmholtz theory postulates three types of
cones, R, G, and B, each containing a slightly variant
substance (chemistry) so that it is maximally sensitive in
a different region of the spectrum. Following the law of
specific energies—in a rough statement of which, incidentally, Young had anticipated Johannes Müller, as is
evident in this color theory—R cones, if stimulated in
isolation, would yield a red sensation, G cones a green
sensation, and so on. The rate of firing for each type of
cone, its excitability, depends upon the wave length of
the stimulating light. *Hue* thus depends on the relative
frequencies of impulses set up in the three types of fibers,
brightness on the total frequency of impulses in all three
fibers, and *saturation* on the amount of white produced
in any fusion, i.e. if a given stimulus elicits 3 R, 8 G,
and 12 B, three units of each will go into the production
of white, leaving 5 G and 9 B to fuse into a somewhat
desaturated greenish blue.

The determination of excitability curves for the three
types of cones seemed a direct enough matter to early
investigators: they had merely to determine by *color mixture* what proportions of the three primary wave lengths
are required to match each portion of the visible spectrum—i.e. the facts of color mixture were assumed to
provide a faithful picture of the composite action of the
three kinds of cones. König and Dieterici (1892) were
the first to make such colorimetric measurements with
sufficient accuracy, and their *Grundempfindungen*—basic
sensation curves—are shown in Fig. 61A. These curves
are several steps removed from direct color-mixture data,
however. In the first place, direct colorimetric matching
of the spectrum shows that at most points one of the
primaries, red, green, or blue, has a *negative value*.
Since it did not seem reasonable that receptors
could respond at *less* than zero frequencies, König and

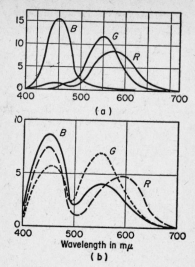

Fig. 61. A. *Grundempfindungen as derived by Koenig and Dieterici from color mixture data.* B. *Grundempfindungen which Helmholtz constructed in order to account for the data of Koenig and Dieterici on hue discrimination.* Hecht, Journal of the Optical Society of America, 1930, 20: 238, 248.

Dieterici (and other subsequent workers) shifted their curves to a level where all values became positive. Secondly, since König assumed that the three primaries contribute equally to the experience of white, the *areas* under the three curves were arbitrarily made equal. Despite these transformations and the mediate character of the data, of which König himself was well aware, these *Grundempfindungen* have often been treated as if they represented direct measurements of the relative rates of the firing of the three types of cones.

If these curves did reflect faithfully the composite action of three types of cones, then other major facts of color vision should also be derivable from them. This is not the case (cf. Hecht, 1930), (a) Since cone responses determine brightness as well as color experience, *adding together excitation curves for the three cone mechanisms should generate the general luminosity curve for cone vision* (i.e. the unimodal curve shown in Fig. 48). A glance at König's basic sensation curves shows that the blue portion of the spectrum would be made disproportionately bright, and the total luminosity function derived in this manner would certainly not be unimodal. To approximate the actual luminosity function for cone vision, the 'blue' excitation curve must be multiplied by a factor of only 0.006, the 'green' curve by 0.426, and the 'red' curve by 0.568 (Ives, 1923). In other words, the contribution of 'blue' to color experience is all out of proportion to its contribution to brightness. (b) Since, according to the Young-Helmholtz theory, white is produced by the combined activity of all three components, *the least well-saturated portions of the spectrum should be those in which the greatest overlap occurs among the three excitation curves.* Since yellow is the least saturated spectral color, overlap should be maximal near 585 mμ, but it is actually greatest about 500 mμ. (c) It will be recalled that the data for *hue discrimination* (see Fig. 49) revealed four regions of maximal differential sensitivity to change in wave length. Helmholtz himself (1891, trans. 1924) was the first to suggest that wavelength discrimination should vary directly with the rate at which spectral sensitivity of the three cone components was changing along the spectrum. For example, if frequency of response for the green cones was changing rapidly between 500 and 510 mμ, differential sensitivity should be fine in this region. This means that *hue discrimination data should be predictable from basic excitation curves.* When Helmholtz tried to derive König and Dieterici's hue discrimination data from their own *Grundempfindungen,* however, he found it impossible and therefore derived a new set, shown as Fig. 61B. It is certain that the excitation ratios of R, G, and B cones as a function of wave length cannot be faithfully represented by *both* sets of *Grundempfindungen.*

In a brilliant theoretical analysis, Hecht (1930) has greatly enhanced the tenability of the Young-Helmholtz theory by describing quantitative functions for a three-cone mechanism from which not only the data of color mixture can be derived but also those of brightness, saturation, and hue discrimination. His excitation curves are shown in Fig. 62, violet (V) being used as the third primary rather than blue for reasons we shall consider later. (a) Hecht's excitation curves are given such values that they summate directly to give the *photopic visibility curve*, i.e. the relative brightness of various portions of the spectrum can be derived from them. (b) Within this limitation, these theoretical curves are further made to intersect in those ways required to account for complementary equations and *the general facts of color mix-*

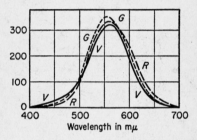

Fig. 62. Basic sensation curves proposed by Hecht to account for brightness-hue discrimination, and saturation thresholds, as well as color mixture data. Hecht, Journal of the Optical Society of America, 1930, 20:252.

ture; R and G curves, for example, cross at 585 mμ to account for yellow. The large amount of overlap among these similar curves, rather than producing white (as in the classic view), is assumed to contribute to the total brightness of experience. (c) For the portion of the spectrum between 400 mμ and 500 mμ, S (saturation) =

$\dfrac{V + G - 2R}{V + G + R}$, and between 500 mμ and 700 mμ,

$\dfrac{G + R - 2V}{V + G + R}$. Where the three components are equal,

S equals zero, or pure white; the greater the dominance of the two hue-producing components over the third white or brightness-producing component, the greater the saturation. Hecht made further slight adjustments in his curves until application of these formulas to them would generate data on *saturation thresholds* obtained by Priest and Brickwedde (1926). (d) Similar minor adjustments made it possible to incorporate data on *hue discrimination* obtained by Laurens and Hamilton (1923).

The reader must also be cautioned that *Hecht's excitation curves do not represent actual measurements of R, G, and V cone-excitation ratios.* Rather, they represent *inferred* characteristics of three postulated cone types, just as did König's *Grundempfindungen.* They are founded on a broader empirical base, however, the insight being that luminosity as well as wave-length functions must be included if such curves are to have any generality. The fact that they yield a precise derivation of several different sets of empirical observations is inconsequential—as Hecht himself repeatedly points out, they were constructed to do exactly this. This in no way detracts from Hecht's contribution; the tenability of any hypothesis varies with the number of relevant phenomena incorporated. The impressiveness of the demonstration lies in the fact that functions for only three-cone mechanisms *can* integrate such a large number of interlocking visual phenomena.

THE PHENOMENOLOGICAL PRIMACY OF YELLOW

Phenomenologists have generally agreed that there are four primary hues, red, *yellow*, green, and blue. Furthermore, although the components can be distinguished in many color mixtures, yellow cannot be analyzed into its red and green components. The same unitary character holds for sensations of white and black. To provide a hypothetical neurological base for such a 'natural' color system, Hering (1920, or see Boring, 1942) postulated three chemical substances in three types of cones, a white-black substance, a yellow-blue substance, and a red-green substance. Breaking down (catabolism) these substances was supposed to yield one type of sensation (e.g. white, yellow, and red), but building up (anabolism) the same substances was supposed to yield the antagonistic sensations (e.g. black, blue, and green). *All* light was necessarily assumed to excite both catabolic and anabolic activities in the white-black substance, yielding a gray whose brightness was a function of the ratio between these processes; otherwise the antagonism between complementary colors, such as yellow and blue, would produce 'nil' rather than neutral gray.

The main reason Hering's theory has not survived is that it runs into such obvious conflict with the law of specific energies. Each cone is asked to distinguish (through the quality of its impulses) between the anabolic and catabolic changes in its chemical substance. In other words, the same fibers must carry both 'yellow impulses' and 'blue impulses,' but according to present-day views sensory fibers are incapable of distinguishing between the stimuli that give rise to them. Since the law of specific energies is by no means certain—as we shall become increasingly aware—Hering's theory is still a possibility. And the existence of independent Y receptors proves to be a popular notion.

COLOR BLINDNESS AND PERIMETRY MEASUREMENTS

Christine Ladd-Franklin, in 1892 (cf. 1929), proposed a theory of color vision that was, in a sense, a compromise between the Young-Helmholtz and the Hering positions. Keeping the phenomenological advantage of Hering's theory, she postulated four primaries (R, G, Y, and B); to avoid collision with the law of specific energies, she postulated separate cone mechanisms for each primary. She was undoubtedly motivated by two often observed difficulties with the Young-Helmholtz view: (1) in the two most common forms of *color blindness* red and green cannot be discriminated but yellow, supposedly produced by the combined action of red and green, is experienced; (2) in *perimeter studies* it has been found that as small patches of either red or green are directed more and more toward the periphery, they turn into *yellow*. How can yellow be experienced at a retinal locus where neither of its presumed components can be? Yellow and blue patches retain their own hues until quite far out toward the periphery, changing finally into achromatic gray. It seems reasonable to suppose that these two sets of facts are related—one might say that the normal eye is red-green blind somewhat peripherally, becoming totally color blind in the extreme periphery.

Color blindness and its implications have long been matters of special interest not only to the layman, because it seems strange that everyday objects may not look the same to others as to him, but also to the philosopher-scientist, because here the 'obvious' relation between stimulus and sensation breaks down. Superficially the Young-Helmholtz theory requires that functional loss of one type of cone will eliminate that component from vision, i.e. a 'green-blind' subject should experience only red-blue hues, a 'red-blind' subject only green-blue hues, and so on. What do the color blind actually experience? Obviously a color-blind person cannot describe for us what he experiences in a language based on sensations he cannot have, but there are rare cases where color blindness is confined to one eye and such individuals can tell us how vision with the color-blind eye differs from that with the normal eye. We find that what appears white to the normal eye also appears white to both red-blind and green-blind eyes; for both red-blind and green-blind eyes the visible spectrum is divided at a neutral point into two hues, *yellow* and blue. Neither of these facts makes sense in an unextended Young-Helmholtz theory.

Let us look briefly at the *varieties of color defect*. Normal color vision is referred to as *trichromatism*, specifying the fact that ordinary individuals require three primaries to match all the spectral hues they can experience. Those who are *protanomalous trichromats* and *deuteranomalous trichromats* also require three primaries, but the former use more red in their mixtures and the latter more green. Actually, there is considerable variability within the normal range, and these anomalous trichromats are merely on the extremes of the continuum. The *protanopic dichromat* (red-blind) and the *deuteranopic dichromat* (green-blind) require only two primaries to match all the hues they can experience. The protanope is relatively insensitive to wave lengths in the 'red' region but relatively more sensitive in the 'blue' region. The deuteranope, on the other hand, is *no* less sensitive than normal to wave lengths in the 'green' region—the term 'green-blind' for this defect is clearly a misnomer. For both protanopes and deuteranopes the spectrum appears blue in the short wave-length portion and yellow in the long wave-length portion, these two bands being divided by a hueless region called the *neutral point*, saturation increasing in both directions from this division. Both protanopes and deuteranopes have difficulty in discriminating reds and greens (or mixtures in which these components serve as differentials to the normal eye). Red-green blindness of one form or the other, by all odds the most common defect, is known to be inherited. It appears some ten times more often in men than in women. *Tritanopia*, a form of dichromatism in which the eye is insensitive to yellow and blue, is a very rare defect associated with diseases of the eye. The *monochromat* is totally color blind, matching all spectral hues solely on the basis of brightness. This is also a very rare defect, representing complete lack of cone vision.

Mrs. Ladd-Franklin linked her four-receptor theory to certain evolutionary facts and was able to give a convincing account of both color blindness and perimetry data. Achromatic rod vision was assumed to be the most primitive form of the light sense (in vertebrates, at any rate). The rod structures evolve into primitive yellow and blue cones, differentially sensitive to long and short wave lengths of the spectrum, respectively. The third evolutionary step is the modification of some of the yellow cones into still further specialized mechanisms, the red and green cones whose chemistries selectively split the spectral region originally spanned by yellow. Note that red and green light combine to yield the sensation characteristic of the parent yellow cone, and yellow and blue light combine to yield the sensation characteristic of achromatic rods. Color blindness represents a throwback to a more primitive condition; since it is well known that the most recently acquired characteristics are the most readily eliminated in such cases, red and green blindness is the most common defect—an *inherited* defect, we recall. And visual experience for these people, appropriately enough, *is* yellow-blue. The final assumption, also buttressed by comparative studies, is that evolution has been most rapid in the foveal area of the eye, itself an advanced structure, slowing down toward the periphery. In other words, various portions of the retina 'recapitulate' the course of evolution—all four types of color receptors are present near the fovea (and red and green patches are discriminated in perimetry experiments); farther out, the yellow cones have not differentiated (and both red and green patches can only excite yellow cones); and still farther out in the most primitive periphery, the rods have not differentiated (and all colored patches are perceived as gray).

What about the Young-Helmholtz theory? Obviously it is incapable of handling these facts in its classic form. An ingenious suggestion, however, originally offered by Fick (1879) and elaborated by Hecht (1930, 1934), solves the problem neatly. Let us assume that protanopes, rather than lacking red cones, have cones in which the photosensitive substance is changed so that their absorption spectrum becomes identical with that for green cones (or vice versa, for deuteranopes). Since the rest of the (neural) mechanism remains unchanged, stimulation of these modified 'red' cones will still yield *red* sensations, but response frequencies to various wave lengths of light will be identical with those for 'green' cones. In such a case any wave length between 500 mμ and 700 mμ would necessarily yield yellow experience (e.g. equal excitation of R and G), desaturated to the extent that the blue mechanism is excited. Any wave length between 400 mμ and 500 mμ would necessarily yield blue experience, desaturated to the extent that fused R and G are excited. But such an eye would be incapable of discriminations on the basis of R and G mixtures, as is the case. The same kind of argument could be given for perimetry data—for some reason, R and G cone chemistries are identical in the medial retina. It should be pointed out, however, that this chemistry shift is a sheer *ad hoc* notion (and it is just as much an additional postulate for the Young-Helmholtz theory as Ladd-Franklin's Y receptor). Furthermore, it offers no ready explanation of the rarity of blue-yellow blindness (tritanopia) or its non-inherited origin.

Ladd-Franklin's evolutionary theory has much to recommend it, yet it has never been as popular as the

Young-Helmholtz view. The reason is *not* that there exists crucial evidence favoring the latter. There are at least three quite different reasons: in the first place, the immense prestige of Helmholtz as a scientist has undoubtedly weighted the scales in favor of the theory he sponsored. Secondly, Hecht's relatively recent demonstration that a three-cone hypothesis can be made to fit a wide swath of relevant data has greatly increased the theory's tenability—although a similar feat would presumably be feasible for a four-cone hypothesis. Thirdly, many students, following the law of parsimony, have concluded that if a three-cone hypothesis can accomplish as much as a four-cone hypothesis, there is no need for the extra (yellow) entity, but it should be kept in mind that the 'law' of parsimony is at best a rough guide, not a scalpel.

INFORMATION AS TO RECEPTOR TYPES

If we had direct information about the nature and number of color receptors—in regard to the existence of an independent Y cone, for example—there would certainly be fewer competing theories in the field. Unfortunately such information is hard to obtain. Cone types do not label themselves histologically; their small size and comparative inaccessibility make direct neurophysiological study difficult—particularly with the human, who alone can tell us what sensations result from the stimulation of certain receptors. And indirect attacks are usually open to several interpretations. Nevertheless, tremendous ingenuity has gone into the search for receptor types, which, after all, is the critical theoretical issue.

(1) *Differential absolute thresholds.* Taking advantage of the fact that there is an achromatic gray interval at low intensities before light is perceived as colored, Göthlin (1944) has made a direct experimental determination of the short wave-length primary in man's color sense. Both Young and Helmholtz had specified violet as the short wave-length fundamental because blue could be obtained by mixing green and violet. Maxwell, on the other hand, had specified blue because it is psychologically a more unitary experience than violet. Using violet hues between

430 and 455 mμ, Göthlin gradually increased intensity from subthreshold levels and noted the points at which both blue and red components of the violet sensation appeared. In all cases the first color experience to arise was *blue*, the sensation becoming violet (e.g. the red component added) at much higher intensities. This would seem to clinch the fact that B is a fundamental, having its own receptors, and violet a compound, unless there is some unknown factor operating here. This method would seem to be applicable to other points along the spectrum as a determinant of fundamentals, but for some reason no further information is available.

(2) *Neutral points of the color blind.* König (1897) thought that the neutral points of the color blind held the answer to cone types. With one type of receptor nonfunctional, the crossing of the *Grundempfindungen* for the other two should yield a white or gray neutral point (assuming the chemical shift discussed above). The fact that the protanopes have a neutral point at 495 mμ, the crossing of G and B functions (see Fig. 46), certainly fits this assumption. But if the third primary be called *blue*, then the R and G functions must cross twice in order to account for the reddish blue of the violet end of the spectrum (refer again to Fig. 46). By this logic, then, a *tritanopic* individual who is presumably deficient in the blue mechanism should show *two* neutral points, one about 460 mμ and the other about 570 mμ. Since König found only one neutral point about 570 mμ, he decided in favor of *violet* as the short wave-length component. Hecht (1930) follows this reasoning in choosing V rather than B for his functions, but he also cites more recent evidence obtained by Dieter in 1927 as showing the predicted second neutral point for tritanopes. To explain the dilemma of a V curve and a B psychological primacy, Hecht suggests that some, say 10 per cent, of the R cones have taken on the spectral characteristics of the substance in the B cones. Light sufficient to excite the B mechanism therefore excites R minimally. In other words, Hecht assumes that all normal eyes are slightly red blind.

(3) *Binocular fusion of yellow.* Hecht (1930) has argued thus: '. . . if red light falls on the retina of one

eye, and green light falls on the corresponding portion of the retina of the other eye, and the result is a yellow sensation, then only Young's idea is tenable.' Hecht reasons that if the yellow experience can be manufactured binocularly in this fashion, there is no need to postulate any Y cone. This reasoning is actually quite faulty. Ladd-Franklin, for example, could agree with the binocular mixture of Y from R and G, and still postulate a separate Y cone for other reasons. The important point is that were binocular production of yellow not possible, then the Young-Helmholtz theory would not be tenable; successful demonstration of the phenomenon does not mean it is the 'only' tenable theory.

After a confusing history of claims and counterclaims (e.g. between Helmholtz, who couldn't get it, and Hering, (who could—which is an interesting reversal), it is gradually becoming clear that central fusion of red and green into yellow can occur. Although Hecht's own demonstration (1928) was soundly criticized by Murray (1939), Prentice (1948) has obtained the phenomenon under conditions that leave little room for doubt. What is probably more puzzling than the fact that binocular fusion of complementaries like red and green can occur is the fact that it is so difficult. In a rather extensive study on binocular mixtures, Pickford (1947) found that although similar colors (e.g. neighboring on the color circle) readily fused, complementaries did so only with great difficulty. In fact, the usual result of such attempts is binocular *rivalry*, not fusion, i.e. first one hue and then the other is centrally 'suppressed.' But why? We know that when intermingled red and green dots are presented to *one* eye, they easily fuse to yellow; we also know that two slightly different visual patterns presented to the *two* eyes fuse to a single contour experience, as in the perception of depth (cf. Chap. 6)—in fact, it is unusual under ordinary conditions that anything other than single vision with the two eyes occurs. What is the difference when corresponding retinal points of the two eyes are stimulated separately with red and green lights? One would expect that *only* binocular fusion could occur.

(4) *Microstimulation of the retina.* Hartridge (1946 *a*, *b*, *c*) has devised an instrument, essentially a micro-

scope used in reverse, which will cast an extremely small image on the retina. He estimates that areas as small as the distance between the centers of adjacent foveal cones can be stimulated in this manner. It is not clear, however, to what extent diffraction in the ocular media and involuntary eye movements would obscure the results here. When such a stimulator is moved slowly across the fovea, hue changes are perceived although the wavelength composition of the stimulus is constant. Monochromatic orange (620 mμ) appears red in some loci and pale orange in others; monochromatic green (540 mμ) appears green, pale green, or even white. An achromatic white light may appear as red, as green or as blue, or as paler intermediaries, depending upon locus. Hartridge was also able to show that the fixation points for the various primary hues were in slightly different places in his own fovea, suggesting a clustering of cones of the same type. The evidence up to this point seems quite compatible with the Young-Helmholtz conception of three-cone types. When a *foveal* luminosity curve was determined with this stimulator, however, two regions of reduced sensitivity appeared, one corresponding to blue and the other to *yellow*. Hartridge considers this evidence for the existence of an independent yellow mechanism, which would be compatible with the Ladd-Franklin hypothesis. Actually, given the extreme amount of overlap among R, G, and V sensation curves as developed by Hecht for the Young-Helmholtz theory (cf. Fig. 62), one would expect nearly any stimulating light to elicit nearly any color experience, depending on what particular receptors happened to be contacted. But this was not the case—for example, monochromatic oranges and yellows never appeared blue.

(5) *Electrophysiological analysis.* Hartridge was trying to obtain the ideal of separately exciting individual receptor elements. Can this be accomplished with electrophysiological techniques? Granit and his various collaborators (summarized in 1947) have devised a technique for use with animal subjects that also approaches this ideal. With the cornea and lens removed, a very fine micro-electrode is inserted into the retina. Electrical activity in one or more *optic fibers* (not receptors, unfortu-

ately) which lie on the retinal surface can then be recorded while the characteristics of the visual stimulus are experimentally varied. The eyes of many different species have been studied in this manner. For a single reading, with the electrode in a stable locus and after appropriate pre-adaptation of the eye, the minimum intensity of light of a given wave length required to produce a just recordable response is determined; by varying the wave length of the stimulus on successive tests, the sensitivity curve for that particular locus is obtained.

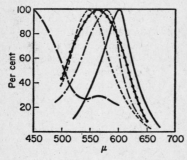

Fig. 63. Sample of modulator curves for light adapted eye of a frog. Granit, Journal of the Optical Society of America, 1941, 31:575.

When an eye was sufficiently dark-adapted, almost any locus was found to yield a *scotopic dominator curve*. This sensitivity curve has its maximum near 500 mμ and closely matches the absorption spectrum for visual purple, i.e. it is the typical rod function. After an eye containing both rods and cones had been sufficiently light-adapted, a *photopic dominator curve* could be obtained from most any locus. It has its maximum near 560 mμ, thus demonstrating the Purkinje shift, and is similar to the cone visibility curve for human observers. Occasionally, after light-adaptation, certain placements of the electrode would yield curves having *narrow* sensitivity ranges. Granit has termed these *photopic modulator curves*. These narrow curves are quite variable in their maxima, but tend to cluster in certain regions of the spectrum

—R modulators (maxima about 600 mμ), rarer Y modulators (about 580 mμ), G modulators (about 530 mμ), and B modulators (about 450 mμ). Figure 63 describes a set of modulator curves for the frog's eye, which is similar to man's in its photopic spectrum, along with the commonly appearing photopic dominator curve.

On the basis of these and other observations Granit (1947, Chaps. 18-22) has developed a theory which is also a kind of compromise between the classic Young-Helmholtz and the Hering positions. Although, like Young, he postulates a limited number of receptors yielding unique sensations (the modulators), he does not restrict himself to three, being quite open to the possibility that there may be more than the four (R, Y, G, B) modulator mechanisms already evident in the data. Like Hering, however, he separates the color and brightness aspects of sensation, attributing the former to modulator action and the latter to dominator action. This separation of color and brightness into two neural mechanisms has certain advantages, as we shall see. Granit's hypothetical excitation curves are shown in Fig. 64. As was the case with Hecht's curves, these functions are so

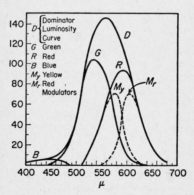

Fig. 64. Basic sensation curves proposed by Granit. The photopic dominator curve (D) is a synthesis of modulator functions. Granit, Sensory Mechanisms of the Retina, Oxford University Press, Inc., New York, 1947, p. 332.

constructed as to summate into the luminosity curve for human day vision. Unlike Hecht's analysis, however, Granit has made no rigorous attempt to integrate the phenomena of color mixture, hue discrimination, spectral saturation, and so on with his hypothetical functions. These curves are chiefly a graphic summary of his electrophysiological findings.

Certain of Granit's observations lead to serious problems. He reports, for example, that 'in a mixed eye a great majority of the units tested will, sooner or later, give a sensitivity curve determined by visual purple. This . . . is evidence that both rods and cones can activate the same nerve fiber' (p. 305). Polyak (1941) has offered histological evidence that cone endings do overlap on bipolar cells, as well as cone and rod endings merging the same way. In fact, Polyak has theorized that the cones must give qualitatively different responses to wave lengths which are 'analyzed' by the bipolar cells. But what will the *sensation* be in such cases? Will one and the same fiber convey 'red' information while its response is being determined by an *R*-cone modulator and then turn about and convey 'white' information when its response is being determined by the rod-dominators? If so, we must discard the law of specific energies of nerve fibers—and, indeed, we may have to do just that. But let us look more closely at Granit's method. He frankly admits there is no guarantee that his micro-electrodes were recording from only a single fiber. Suppose that the electrodes were actually picking up activity from a small *group* of fibers, and keep in mind that his method (noting just-recordable response) was one that selects the most sensitive elements for a given condition: under conditions of bright-adaptation the fiber for a 'red' modulator under the electrode would determine the sensitivity function but, as the eye became dark-adapted, fibers for rod dominators would come to determine the function. In such a case, the Purkinje shift obtained at a single locus would not necessarily refute the specific energies law.

But what about the modulator curves themselves? These relatively narrow and widely separated sensitivity functions bear no resemblance to Hecht's fundamental curves for *R*, *G*, and *V* cones, and, whereas Hecht's functions are purely hypothetical, these modulator curves at least approximate recordings from individual fibers. *If Granit's observations on modulator functions prove to be valid as indicators of the spectral sensitivities of different types of cones, then Hecht's analysis and the theory it supports must go by the board.* But again we must look into the method. Threshold observations are tricky matters, requiring extremely rigid control over both the degree of pre-adaptation and the length of time following at which observations are made. The fact that individual curves for the same modulator in the same species often showed considerable variation in maxima suggests the existence of considerable errors in measurement. It doesn't seem at all likely that receptor chemistries for the same modulator mechanism could vary sufficiently to account for these differences. On the other hand, although we have no guarantee that single fibers were being measured here, it would be difficult to explain the *narrow* sensitivity curves on this basis. Observations of this order constitute a serious challenge to the adequacy of the Young-Helmholtz theory.

BRIGHTNESS AND COLOR VISION

As was noted earlier in this chapter, *saturation varies with intensity*. If the intensity of monochromatic light is raised above or lowered below the optimal level, the saturation of the color experience decreases. And even with strictly foveal stimuli, all wave lengths of light except extreme spectral red evoke colorless, gray experience if the intensity is lowered sufficiently (Purdy, as reported in Troland, 1930, pp. 167-8). The intensity range through which chromatic stimuli yield colorless experience is called the *photochromatic interval* (a better term would be the *achromatic interval*), and it has been shown to be widest for short wave lengths and narrowest for long ones, wider in the periphery than in the fovea. A special case of the relation between saturation and intensity is *chromatic summation*: as the area of a stimulus is reduced to very small size, saturation decreases toward gray (i.e. areal summation holds for color as well as for brightness). Color theorists have paid little attention to these well-known facts, yet they pose serious problems for views of the Young-Helmholtz and Ladd-Franklin types. Why should the quality of sensation correlated with activity in 'green' fibers change from green to gray merely because the frequency of impulses in them is reduced? The change from green to gray implies a shift in 'what' fibers are delivering impulses, but neither of these theories puts 'white' receptors in the fovea. Granit has no difficulty here: since the white dominators have a wider sensitivity range than the more specialized modulators, increasing or decreasing intensity from the optimum shifts the population of receptors excited in favor of the dominators; reducing the area of stimulation decreases the probability of contacting the less numerous modulators and hence 'whitens' the sensation.

The study of *chromatic adaptation* has had an extensive but mottled history (cf. Cohen, 1946 b). The general procedure is to expose a part of the retina to a constant 'fatiguing' stimulus and measure changes in saturation, hue, and brightness as a function of time, using a fresh region of the retina as a basis for comparison. All investigators agree that there is loss of saturation under continued stimulation. This would be expected in terms of all the theories we have considered, since the more intensely excited receptors should adapt most rapidly, balancing the color equation and 'whitening' the experience. All theories would also predict a loss in brightness, owing to a total reduction in impulse frequency. Although it is true that many investigators have obtained this result, the most recent and carefully executed experiment in the area (Cohen, 1946 a) describes an actual *increase* in brightness. This implies an increase in the total impulse frequency during chromatic adaptation—as if reduction in rate of fire in the dominant mechanism were releasing other mechanisms from inhibition. We shall return to this matter of inhibitory mechanisms at a later point. Finally, these theories would predict a shift in hue during the course of adaptation, a shift toward certain 'basic colors' as stable points: suppose R and G cones (or modulators) are firing in the ratio of 2 to 1 for an orange stimulus; the more rapid reduction in R impulses will produce not only a loss in saturation but also a shift in hue toward the green region. Again, most investigators report this phenomenon, but Cohen found no consistent shifts in hue during adaptation. Unless Cohen's results can be explained away as the results of some artifact (which this reviewer, at least, is unable to discover), they constitute negative evidence for existing theories.

What about brightness functions for the color blind—

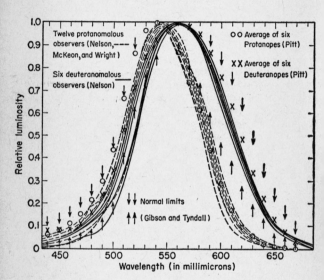

Fig. 65. *Relative luminosity functions of anomalous trichromats (six deuteranomalous, twelve protanomalous) compared with averages for dichromats and with limits for normal trichromats.* Judd, Journal of the Optical Society of America, 1943, 33:303.

do they offer any information for an evaluation of color theories? Figure 65 combines the data of several studies, showing *luminosity functions* for several types of color blindness as well as the range considered normal. Protanopes, to be sure, have reduced sensitivity in the red region, but they have also relatively increased sensitivity to light in the blue region. Deuteranopes, who presumably should show reduced sensitivity in the green region,

actually return a luminosity curve that falls well within
the normal range. Another interesting point in these
data is that protanomalous trichromats show nearly as
much deviancy in sensitivity to red light as do the protanopic dichromats, yet the former vary from normal behavior only in the proportions of their color mixtures.
The *saturation of the spectrum* for color defectives has
been studied by Chapanis (1944), using absolute saturation thresholds at nineteen spectral points as a measure.
All types of color blindness were shown to suffer loss in
saturation throughout the spectrum, as compared with
normal controls. For the deuteranope this means that a
marked loss in saturation of the spectrum can occur
without any concurrent abnormality in brightness sensitivity. Chapanis (1946, 1947) has also studied *dark*
adaptation in the color deficient. Whereas both protanopes and deuteranopes returned normal dark-adaptation functions when a *violet* test light was used, and
deuteranopes were also normal with a *red* test light, the
adaptation curves of *protanopes* to *red* light revealed a
novel and previously unreported effect: after about 12
minutes in the dark, during which time little adaptation
occurs, the protanopic retina suddenly begins to adapt
further to red light, reaching a final level that is essentially normal. Since this effect fails to appear when the
red stimulus is restricted to the foveal, rod-free area,
Chapanis concludes that 'the rods are sensitive to red
light, but . . . this cannot be observed in the color
normal individual because his cones are at least equally
as sensitive to red as are his rods.'

Even in its contemporary form, the Young-Helmholtz
theory has trouble with these data. From the close overlap of Hecht's sensation curves, it can be seen that the
mere shift in cone chemistry (R cones to G or vice versa)
should cause little change in luminosity functions. This
fits the deuteranope but not the protanope—Hecht
(1934) frankly admits the inadequacy of the three-cone
hypothesis on this point. Chapanis finds no support in
his saturation data for either the classic or the contemporary version of the Young-Helmholtz theory. Since
basic sensation curves for the Ladd-Franklin view have
never been worked out rigorously, it cannot be said

whether it would cover these data or not. By virtue of its dissociation of hue and brightness mechanisms, Granit's dominator-modulator theory is in a better position. The deuteranope lacks the 'green' modulator, but his photopic dominator system is normal; the protanope lacks the 'red' modulator and his photopic dominator system is also deficient. The deuteranope's marked loss in saturation without concomitant reduction in brightness sensitivity also becomes understandable. But why should protanopia alone be associated with malfunctioning dominators and why should the curve have the form it does? Jahn (1946) suggests that dominator functions are recorded from giant ganglion cells which have multisynaptic connections with both rods and all types of cones, whereas modulator functions are recorded from midget ganglion cells (cf. Polyak, 1941) which are associated with single cones via single bipolar cells. In deuteranopia it is the 'green' midget ganglia that are nonfunctional, but since the 'green' cones still contribute to dominator channels via the giant multisynaptic ganglia, the luminosity curve is unaffected. In protanopia it is the 'red' cones that are nonfunctional, and hence both 'red' modulator activity and luminosity in the red region are affected.

DO THE RODS PLAY ANY ROLE IN COLOR VISION?

Although it is generally agreed that at least three mechanisms must participate in color vision, it is not necessary that all three be cones in the usual sense. Several writers have toyed with the idea that the rods may contribute to color vision. The most detailed development of this notion has been made by Willmer (1946). Noting the lack of anatomical evidence for different types of cones, he specifies a single type of cone which contributes the R component. Ordinary dark-adapting rods are assumed to contribute a B component and a class of nonadapting day rods contributes the third component. Since the central fovea is supposed to have only cones and nonadapting rods (i.e. is diplodic), it is relatively blue-blind and prone to hue-discrimination confusions when intensity is varied. How these three mechanisms combine in the production of white is not entirely clear.

There is considerable indirect evidence suggesting an identification of the B component of color vision with a rodlike mechanism. In the first place, Pieron (1932, as reported in Granit, 1947) has shown that the 'rising time' (reaction latency) for perceiving stimulation is longest for blue light and shortest for red light; it will be recalled that in the ERG, as well as in the electrical response of the optic nerve, activity attributable to rods showed a longer latency than that attributable to cones. Adrian (1945) has recorded ERG's from his own eye.

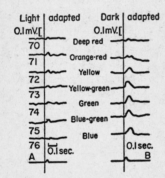

Fig. 66. ERG's for various wave lengths in (A) light-adapted and (b) dark-adapted human eyes. Adrian, Journal of Physiology, 1945, 104:89.

When stimulating the peripheral retina, he found a brief diphasic response to characterize the cone mechanism (e.g. after bright adaptation) and a monophasic response to characterize the rod mechanism (e.g. after dark adaptation). Using color filters of known transmission values, the response to deep red was then found to be a pure cone affair, as would be predicted, and that to blue revealed *only* the rod component, which would not be predicted from most theories. Intermediary stimuli displayed the effects of both mechanisms. These results are shown in Fig. 66. Granit (1947, p. 341) adds this bit of evidence: a blue modulator function is prominent in the pure rod retina of the guinea pig but absent in the pure cone retina of the snake. Whether the foveal area is in fact 'blue-blind' or tritanopic is very much a matter of controversy in the recent literature (cf. Craik, 1943; Willmer, 1944; Willmer and Wright, 1945; Hartridge, 1944, 1945*a*).

Some facts about *after-images* are germane to this discussion. If a black-and-white figure is fixated for a few seconds under high illumination and one then looks at a neutral gray paper, a negative after-image will be seen, the brightness relations of the original now being reversed. If a colored patch is used as a stimulus, the after-image is typically in the complementary hue. Both of these phenomena point to selective adaptation of the visual receptors. Depending on their excitation characteristics, different receptor types respond at different rates to the original stimulus and hence adapt to different degrees; when a uniform field is then substituted, these receptors fire at *different* rates depending on their states of adaptation, and yield a reversed (brightness and/or hue) image. Furthermore, as might be expected from Pieron's latency data above, the after-effects of a brief flash of white light are not achromatic, but rather appear as a 'flight of colors'—which, for some unknown reason, do not have any regular order of appearance (cf. Woodworth, 1938).

The after-effects above depend upon prolonged or intense stimulation and are persistent enough to be easily observed. Following any retinal stimulation, however, there is a very rapid series of after-effects which are of considerable theoretical interest but are difficult to study. Normally we are unaware of them. These fleeting events can be disentangled by *moving the light stimulus across the retina*, thus translating temporal effects into spatial terms. Bidwell (1898), one of the first to use this method, reported that pale, bluish semicircles seemed to float along behind a circular, white stimulus, these coming to be known as 'Bidwell's Ghosts.' Investigators using this method (McDougall, 1904; Fröhlich, 1921, 1922; Karwoski and Crook, 1937; Karwoski and Warrener, 1942) describe the following sequence of events following a brief stimulus: (1) a very fleeting positive after-

nage of the same hue as the original, called the *Hering
nage,* with a latency of about one-twentieth of a second;
2) following a dark interval, a second positive image
ppears which is called the *Purkinje image,* sometimes
omplementary in hue but usually bluish, with a latency
f about one-fifth of a second; (3) further oscillations of
onger phase and reduced intensity occur. The Purkinje
fter-image has a long latency, becomes increasingly
rominent as illumination is lowered, is predominantly
lue in hue, and is difficult to obtain with extreme red
ght or on the fovea—all these facts suggest involvement
f the rod mechanism. It is true that Karwoski and
Varrener (1942) report obtaining this image with red
ght, and unbrokenly when a slit is moved across the
oveal region, but the red stimulus was somewhat orange
nd the image had a 'bulge' (e.g. even longer latency)
hen crossing the fovea. If the fovea be considered a
olind spot' with respect to rod vision, this bulge may
epresent a filling in of the form at some higher level in
he projection system where the foveal 'gap' is eliminated.

The biggest single stumbling block for Willmer's posi-
ion is that he specifies the dark-adapting rods as con-
ributing the *B* component. It will be recalled that
Granit has shown a correlation between the regeneration
f about 50 per cent maximum visual purple and the
ppearance of the rod component in the *ERG;* the ways
n which the 'hump' in the dark-adaptation curve can
e shifted in latency by manipulating the wave length
nd intensity of pre-adapting and test lights also fits the
iew that the 'ideal' rods are not functional in day vision.
Ve might also note that the onset of the rod 'limb' of
he dark-adaptation curve is accompanied by simple de-
aturation of the hue of a colored stimulus patch, not a
orogressive 'bluing' before turning white, which Will-
ner's theory should demand.

There is, however, another way a rodlike mechanism
an be brought into the picture. Suppose we relegate
Granit's 'ideal,' dark-adapting rods to simple night-vision
unctions, but identify his 'conelike' rods with the *B* com-
oonent in color vision. We should then have to postulate
wo types of cones, *R* and *G,* as a minimum. If we
urther assume that these rodlike receptors are present in

the fovea yet have their maximum density some 7° to 10° eccentric (rather than 20°, as the 'ideal' rods), then certain other facts fall in line. Optimum form perception in the dark-adapted eye has a higher threshold as well as a more central locus on the retina than sheer brightness perception. Even in the fovea, saturation decreases as intensity is lowered below an optimum, and there is an achromatic interval, widest in the blue region of the spectrum and narrowest in the red region, where experi-ence is neutral gray. We also have to assume here that these conelike rods have a wider intensity range than cones proper. In Ladd-Franklin's evolutionary scheme the conelike rods (or rodlike cones) would be the first step in the development of true cones, more specialized in their intensity coverage and neural connections than primitive rods but retaining the spectral characteristics of rods and their slower latency. Why should these mecha-nisms yield achromatic experience rather than blue experi-ence when stimulated alone (e.g. at low intensities)? Actually, all color vision theories agree that hue depends upon the *ratio* of rates of fire in several mechanisms, quite independent of the quality mediated by any mecha-nism alone. These conelike rods could yield achromatic experience when firing alone and yet *modulate* a complex experience toward 'blue' when fused with the excitation of R and G cones.

INHIBITORY PROCESSES IN COLOR VISION?

We have already uncovered some evidence for inhibi-tory mechanisms in color vision. Cohen's (1946 *a*) demonstration that adaptation to monochromatic light was accompanied by an over-all increase in total bright-ness suggested the release of certain mechanisms from inhibition. The fact that protanopes apparently have somewhat heightened sensitivity in the blue region of the spectrum, as compared with normals (Hecht, 1930), has similar implications. And most significantly, it will be recalled that the direct data of colorimetric matching of the spectrum indicate something other than simple addition of excitation is involved. At nearly all loci along the spectrum except those representing the wave length f the primaries themselves, some one component must ave a *negative value* (i.e. must be added to the spectral est patch) if saturation is to be equated.

Basing his argument chiefly on the occurrence of these egative values in colorimetric equations, Göthlin (1943) as developed a theory which, like the Young-Helmholtz iew, utilizes R, G, and B receptors but which also in- ludes inhibitory processes. As shown in Fig. 67, excita- ory and inhibitory effects are conceived as a system of alances: R and G are mutually inhibitory, their cancel- ation or balance yielding the yellow sensation; R and G ogether are mutually inhibitory with B, the total balance

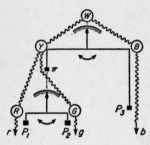

ig. 67. *Diagrammatic representation of Göthlin's inhibitory process theory as a system of interlocking balances— here as arranged in the production of white sensory quality.* Göthlin, American Journal of Psychology, 1943, 56:546.

ielding the white sensation. Complementary after-images re cited as evidence. Strong green light, for example, xcites the G receptors maximally, simultaneously in- ibiting R (first balance) and B (total balance); upon emoval of the green light and consequent release from ihibition of both R and B components, a complemen- ry purple after-image is seen. In ordinary color vision, npulses from R and G, in varying proportions, account or all sensations between red and green, their equality ielding yellow; impulses in B interact with those in the rst balance, yielding violets and purples if the first alance is weighted toward R and yielding blue-greens if he first balance is weighted toward G. This is an attrac-

tively simple theory, but its assumption that R G and
are *mutually* inhibitory runs into difficulty.

Close inspection of Wright's colorimetric matchir
data (cf. Fig. 46) indicates that while B is successful
inhibited by R and possibly by G, R *is inhibited l
neither G nor B*. In interpreting these curves it must b
realized that the negative values for a component actual
indicate *lack* of inhibition, i.e. this component was e
cited in mixing the other two wave lengths and henc
is present to desaturate the experience. Near 500 mμ, f
example, both G and B are vigorously excited in the pr
duction of blue-green, but R must be added to th
spectral patch in order to match saturation, i.e. R mech;
nisms were *not* inhibited in this mixture. To this w
may add some highly relevant neurophysiological info
mation. Granit (1947, pp. 113-14) definitely conside
P111 in the ERG to represent retinal inhibitory pro
esses, and this component of the ERG has been ident
fied with cone pathways. Adrian (1945) has shown tha
the negative component of the ERG is most pronounce
for red stimulation, decreasing as wave length of th
stimulus is shifted toward blue. Secondly, we have ev
dence that fibers in the optic nerve vary in diamet
(Bishop, 1933), larger fibers being generally associate
with a more rapid rate of impulses, and we found in th
preceding section that the B mechanism displays the lor
latency characteristic of small-fiber systems. Finally, it ha
been shown (Bishop and O'Leary, 1938) that the larg
fast-rate fibers deliver their impulses chiefly to the opt
cortex; Adrian (1946) reports that although red ligh
readily yields a large cortical response, blue light produce
no detectable effect here.

This admittedly sketchy information suggests a mod
fication of Göthlin's view which is more nearly in ac
cord with evidence for a rodlike mechanism as the I
component. In connection with an earlier analysis c
brightness summation, inhibition, and acuity, it wa
shown that these phenomena could be incorporated b
the simple assumption that inhibition of locus *a* upon
locus *b* occurs when the frequency of impulses receive
laterally at *b* is more rapid than that received directl
through its projection pathways. If we assume that latera

connections exist between the different color-producing mechanisms, which seems most likely, then the same hypothesis would apply here: *B activity would be inhibited to the extent that R activity is present because of the latter's more rapid impulse rate.* By the same token, any factor that diminishes the rate of fire in R fibers should 'release' the B component. At the neurophysiological level the 'off-effect' in the ERG represents such a 'release'—it is prominent in the response to red light but absent in the response to blue. The increased total brightness during adaptation found by Cohen might represent a similar effect. The fact that protanopia is accompanied by both a decided shift in luminosity of the spectrum and relatively enhanced brightness in the *blue* region, while deuteranopia is not, also becomes more understandable if we assume that an elimination of R impulses has 'released' the B mechanism from inhibition. All this is very hypothetical, but then, color vision is still the happy hunting grounds for theorists.*

SUMMARY

The Young-Helmholtz theory of color vision is the most widely accepted view among psychologists today. It has the twin advantages of simplicity and Hecht's quantification. It runs into a number of difficulties, however. In order to account for the experiences of the color blind, it must postulate a variety of shifts in cone chemistries on an *ad hoc* basis. Ladd-Franklin's theory, which adds a yellow cone and an evolutionary rationale, does better here. But both of these views have trouble with brightness functions of both normals and color blind: why should color experiences become less saturated (a change of quality toward 'white') as intensity is lowered? why should protanopes have a markedly distorted lumi-

---

* Unexpected confirmation of this interpretation has recently been found in an as yet unpublished study by J. Cohen and W. A. Gibson. Analysis of the color space by the theory of invariants showed, among other things, that one receptor must be completely an inhibitor while the other two are completely excitors, or vice versa—in either case, some inhibitory process is required.

nosity curve but deuteranopes a normal one? Gra
dominator-modulator theory works much better here
cause of its separation of color and brightness funct
And if Granit's basic observations on the lumino
functions of individual optic nerve fibers (?) prove va
Hecht's theoretical sensation curves and the theory t
support must be discarded. Finally, there is considera
evidence that the B component in color vision has qu
different properties than either R or G components
fact, properties decidedly rodlike in nature. Willmer
developed a theory on this basis which postulates
one kind of cone interacting with two types of
adapting and nonadapting. A similar possibility was
gested here: namely, that there are only two typ
cones, R and G, with the B component being
tributed by a 'conelike' nonadapting rod.

All of these theories relegate the actual determina
of hue sensations to some process of fusion in the hi
centers, probably the visual cortex. When, for examp
we look at a patchwork quilt of many colors, a differe
ratio of impulses in several fiber types is produced with
each patch as subjectively represented. We speak glibly
about central 'interpretation' of color at this point, bu
this is merely a confession of complete ignorance in regard to mechanism—there is no 'little man' up there
busily noting down incoming frequencies at all loci and
judging their ratios. It must be a remarkable mechanism,
however, unlike anything we know of in other modalities
(except, possibly, olfaction). According to Le Gros Clark
(1947), in the course of projection from retina to brain
three fiber types coming from corresponding points of the
two eyes are segregated in bands in the geniculates and
passed up to each cortical locus having unique spatial
reference. Somehow, at each one of these cortical loci,
ratios of impulse rates channeling upon common synapses
become a variety of experienced hues.

VAN NOSTRAND INSIGHT BOOKS

THE CRISIS IN PSYCHIATRY AND RELIGION—Mowrer
INSTINCT—Birney and Teevan
REINFORCEMENT—Birney and Teevan
COLOR VISION—Teevan and Birney
TOWARD A PSYCHOLOGY OF BEING—Maslow
MEASURING HUMAN MOTIVATION—Birney and Teevan
EMOTION—Candland
PROGRAMMED LEARNING—Smith and Moore
TRANSFER OF LEARNING—Grose and Birney
CONTEMPORARY RESEARCH IN LEARNING—Braun
RESEARCH IN PSYCHOPATHOLOGY—Quay
PSYCHOLOGY IN THE WRY—Baker
RACE, SCIENCE AND HUMANITY—Montagu
PRIMATE SOCIAL BEHAVIOR—Southwick
THE NEW GROUP THERAPY—Mowrer
THE ENCAPSULATED MAN—Royce
THE TRANSPARENT SELF—Jourard
THE PSYCHOPATH—McCord and McCord
THEORIES OF MOTIVATION IN LEARNING—Teevan and Birney
THEORIES OF MOTIVATION IN PERSONALITY AND SOCIAL
PSYCHOLOGY—Teevan and Birney
THE ROOTS OF CONSCIOUSNESS—McClelland
ANTHROPOLOGY—Mead
CONVERSATIONS WITH CARL JUNG—Evans
PERSONALITY AND SCIENCE—McCurdy
SCIENCE AND THEORY IN PSYCHOANALYSIS—Sarason
PSYCHOANALYSIS AND STUDY OF BEHAVIOR—Sarason
FRUSTRATION AND CONFLICT: Selected Readings—Yates
THE EXPERIENCE OF PSYCHOTHERAPY—Fitts
UNDERSTANDING MENTAL HEALTH—Sutherland and Smith
COGNITIVE PROCESSES AND THE BRAIN—Milner and
Glickman
ANIMAL DRIVES—Cicala
INTERPERSONAL ACCOMMODATION—Abrahamson
WARD H—Colarelli and Siegel
ATTENTION—Bakan
RECONCILIATION—Jourard and Overlade, editors
PSYCHOLOGICAL NEEDS AND CULTURAL SYSTEMS—Aronoff
LANGUAGE AND THOUGHT—Hildum, editor
PSYCHOLOGICAL PERSPECTIVES ON THE PERSON—Tallent
HORMONES AND BEHAVIOR—Whalen
CREATIVITY AND CONFORMITY—Moustakas

About this book:

This anthology of original sources on color vision, an endurin
problem in psychology, is concerned with the way in which ma
perceives color. The first section of the book presents reading
from the classical theorists of color vision, from Thomas Young t
Christine Ladd-Franklin. The editors use color blindness as a
evaluation of theories, since all the theorists come to grips wit
this problem. The second section surveys various approaches t
color perception from the 1920's to the present, concluding wit
a final article describing the exciting new discoveries made b
Edwin Land in color vision experiments. Illustrated and docu
mented.

VAN NOSTRAND INSIGHT BOOKS

Insight Books are devoted to filling a vital need in the efficient stud
human behavior. By making available, in paperback, essential mat
that are frequently inaccessible or often neglected in a more expe
form, the Insight Series renders a valuable service to students, teac
and interested laymen. Drawn from psychology and its allied fields
bulk of the books published will deal with the following catego
1) studies of enduring problems in psychology through original sou
2) selections from their own works by contemporary behavioral scien
and 3) authoritative discussions of timely, even controversial, is

DAVID C. McCLELLAND is general editor of Insight Books. Curr
Professor of Psychology and Chairman of the Staff of the Cente
Research in Personality at Harvard University, he is also an establ
author in experimental and theoretical psychology. His new book, '
ACHIEVING SOCIETY, will be published by Van Nostrand.

Along with Dr. McClelland, Dr. Robert C. Birney of Amherst Co
and Dr. Richard C. Teevan of Bucknell University are jointly respo
for editing and developing those books in this series devoted to End
Problems in Psychology.

VAN NOSTRAND   INSIGHT BOO
120 Alexander Street   Princeton, N. J.